A Treasury of
MARK TWAIN

A Treasury of
MARK TWAIN

Introduction by Roy Blount Jr
Illustrated by Rod Waters

LONDON
The Folio Society
1999

Mark Twain's essays, sketches and short stories were frequently reprinted during his lifetime (sometimes in slightly revised versions) in a variety of periodicals and collections. It is therefore sometimes difficult to establish the place and date of first publication of a particular version with absolute certainty, and so no attempt has been made to supply such information here. Where an extract from one of Twain's larger works, *The Innocents Abroad* (1869), *Roughing It* (1872), *The Adventures of Tom Sawyer* (1876), or *A Tramp Abroad* (1880), has been included, the appropriate volume's title has been given at the end of the piece.

First published by The Folio Society Ltd 1999

The Folio Society Ltd
44 Eagle Street
London WC1R 4FS
www.foliosociety.com

Set in Goudy at The Folio Society
Printed on Abbey Wove paper at
Martins the Printers Ltd, Berwick-upon-Tweed,
and bound by Hunter & Foulis, Edinburgh, in
cloth printed with a design by the artist

Thirteenth printing 2011

Contents

Illustrations

Introduction

What is so great about Mark Twain? Here, from one of his several accounts of an earthquake in San Francisco:

The Pastor of Starr King's church, the Rev. Mr Stebbins, came down out of his pulpit after the first shock and embraced a woman. It was an instance of great presence of mind. Some say the woman was his wife, but I regard the remark as envious and malicious. Upon occasions like this, people who are too much scared to seize upon an offered advantage are always ready to depreciate the superior judgment and sagacity of those who profited by the opportunity they lost themselves.

Mark Twain wrote that in 1865. I submit that it is still funny. From another of his stories about that earthquake:

A young gentleman who lives in Sacramento Street rushed downstairs and appeared in public with no raiment on save a knit undershirt, which concealed his person about as much as its tin-foil cap conceals a champagne bottle. He struck an attitude such as a man assumes when he is looking up, expecting danger from above, and bends his arm and holds it aloft to ward off possible missiles – and standing thus he glared fiercely up at the fire-wall of a tall building opposite, from which a few bricks had fallen. Men shouted at him to go in the house, people seized him by the arm and tried to drag him away – even tender-hearted women (O, Woman! . . . in our hours of ease uncertain, coy, and hard to please – when anything happens to go wrong with our harness, a ministering angel thou), women, I say, averted their faces, and nudging the paralyzed and impassible statue in the ribs with their elbows beseeched him to take their aprons – to take their shawls – to take their hoop-skirts – anything, anything, so that he would not stand there longer in such a plight and distract people's attention from the earthquake. But he wouldn't budge – he stood there in his naked majesty till the last tremor died away from the earth, and then looked around on the multitude – and stupidly enough, too, until his dull eye fell upon himself. He went back upstairs, then. He went up lively.

Am I going to tell you that Mark Twain is so great because he could in the same breath both mock and sympathize, by virtue of a homespun aestheticism transcending all conventional sentiment; or because he could evoke both stasis and hullabaloo, prudery and lubricity, microcosm and macrocosm, at once, offhandedly? Or am I going to clarify him psychologically in such terms as these (resorted to by a severe academic critic named Guy Cardwell): 'By temperament and as a jokester . . . he had strongly ego-syntonic as well as syntonic tendencies. Jokes are among the devices which make the resulting stresses bearable'?

I am not.

I put it to you simply that the most impressive thing about Mark Twain is, he is still funny.

Aside from his masterpiece, *Huckleberry Finn* – from which, Ernest Hemingway famously remarked, all of modern American literature springs – none of Twain's books, taken as a whole, is a triumph of form. *Life on the Mississippi*, magnificent in stretches, is more irregular altogether than the river. *Innocents Abroad* and the other travel books are padded-out congeries of tangents and digressions. *Puddin'head Wilson* still shows odd traces of what it started out to be, a shaggy-dog tale of Siamese twins. And what makes *Huckleberry Finn* the template of American narrative is not the novel's construction but its voice – an unprecedented, brilliantly seamless *e pluribus unum* of formal English and several varieties of vernacular American. The voice of a humorist coming to grips (inevitably not to everyone's, indeed perhaps not quite to anyone's, complete satisfaction) with the most indigestible matter of American history: slavery. As a whole it is problematic. Needs constantly to be reconsidered. Which means we can keep going back to enjoy its parts. Consider the perfectly straightforward-sounding sentence, above, 'The Pastor . . . came down out of his pulpit after the first shock and embraced a woman.' In neither the choice nor the sequence of words is there anything like an elbow in our ribs, but as the full stop falls into place do you not share with me a *frisson* of anticipation? We can dip into *Huckleberry Finn* at any point and hear Huck's voice setting us up in the same way again and again.

I wonder in fact how often any of Twain's books are read straight through today. It is at the level of sentence, paragraph, observation, episode and sketch that he is a great and abidingly popular writer. And yet his short humorous pieces usually get short shrift in assessments of his work. He himself, as a young man, deprecated his essential gift: 'I have had a "call" to literature, of a low order – i.e, humorous. It is nothing to be proud of, but it is my strongest suit . . . to excite the *laughter* of God's creatures. Poor, pitiful business!'

Comedy is one thing. Aristophanes is still, and even in uninspired translation, great comedy. But there is virtually no such thing as classic humor. Humor almost always travels badly from culture to culture and perishes fast. What writing in English has remained funny on the page, on its own terms, as long as Twain's? Much of Dickens. Bits of Swift and Sterne and Goldsmith and Dr Johnson. When we read passages of Shakespeare we may smile, but mostly in admiration of how rollicking, how intricately off-hand, great iambic pentameters with the touch of nature can be. Mozart may tickle us comparably, and indeed humor may somehow be a matter of music. When Twain's wife tried to show him how horrid his language around home sometimes was by repeating back to him a string of profanity he had uttered, he told her that she had the words right, but not the tune. The harmonics of Mark Twain's prose . . .

At this point despair begins to creep in. How much can be said about how funny anyone's writing is? Or should be said? Introduce something by going on and on about how funny it is, and the reader may well begin to think, irritably, and quite rightly, 'Perhaps I should be the judge of that.' Laughter is so gratifying because it is autonomic. 'Nothing is so hopeless', Dr Johnson observed, 'as a scheme of merriment.' Merriment bubbles, or not.

But let me quote from Twain's essay on his friend William Dean Howells, a passage about Howells's humor. The tribute seems overgenerous as applied to Howells, but not as it might apply to Twain himself:

I do not think anyone else can play with humorous fancies so gracefully and delicately and deliciously as [Howells] does, nor can come so near making them look as if they were doing the playing themselves and he was not aware that they were at it . . . His is a humor which flows softly all around about and over and through the mesh of the page, pervasive, refreshing, health-giving, and makes no more show and no more noise than does the circulation of the blood.

How universal is this refreshment? Is Twain's humor less accessible to non-American readers of English? Widely traveled as he was, Twain's sensibility was not cosmopolitan. He took unalloyed pleasure in Francophobia (the very word *French*, as he uses it, seems to glow with distaste). The only thing that delighted him about German culture, aside from the manure piles of the Black Forest ('Manure is evidently the Black-Forester's main treasure – his coin, his pride, his Old Master, his ceramics, his bric-a-brac, his darling, his title to public consideration . . . and his first solicitude when he gets ready to make his will') was the national sentence structure:

An average sentence, in a German newspaper, is a sublime and impressive curiosity; it occupies a quarter of a column; it contains all the ten parts of speech – not in regular order, but mixed; it is built mainly of compound words constructed by the writer on the spot, and not to be found in any dictionary – six or seven words compacted into one, without joint or seam . . . it treats of fourteen or fifteen different subjects, each enclosed in a parenthesis of its own, with here and there extra parentheses which re-enclose three or four of the minor parentheses, making pens within pens: finally, all the parentheses and reparentheses are massed together between a couple of king-parentheses, one of which is placed in the first line of the majestic sentence and the other in the middle of the last line of it – *after which comes the* VERB, and you find out for the first time what the man has been talking about; and after the verb – merely by way of ornament, as far as I can make out – the writer shovels in '*haben sind gewesen gehabt haben geworden sein*', or words to that effect, and the monument is finished.

England, however, was one of his favorite countries. To be sure he damned Sir Walter Scott's novels for inflating aristocratic romanticism in the antebellum South (a part of the country which Twain seldom regarded with anything approaching fondness after he left it, heading westward, as a young man, two weeks of highly irregular military service having been enough of the Civil War for his taste). He mocked chivalry and royalty in *Huckleberry Finn* and *A Connecticut Yankee in King Arthur's Court*. But he spent nearly three years altogether in London, where he was lionized. After Oxford granted him an honorary degree, he seized every opportunity to wear the robe that came with it. He absorbed a great deal of English literature in his youth, some of it while learning to pilot a riverboat from a man who interspersed recitations from Shakespeare with imprecations and instruction:

Approach thou *what* are you laying in the leads for? what a hell of an idea! like the rugged ease her off a little, ease her off! rugged Russian bear, the armed rhinoceros or the *there* she goes! meet her, meet her! didn't you know she'd smell the reef if you crowded it like that? Hyrcan tiger . . .

And yet that acute and droll English critic, V. S. Pritchett, in a collection of essays published in 1942, reduced all that was valuable of Mark Twain to one book:

Out of the mess which Twain made of his life, amid the awful pile of tripe which he wrote, there does rise one book which has the serenity of a thing of genius. *Huckleberry Finn* takes the breath away . . . Twain has . . . become the channel of the generic American emotion which floods all really American literature – nostalgia . . . D. H. Lawrence called this feeling the longing of the rebel for a master. It may be simply the longing for a spiritual home . . . And once Mark Twain passed this exquisite moment of his maturity, he went to bits in that morass of sentimentality, cynicism, melodrama and vulgarity which have damned him for the adult reader.

Certainly there is 'sentimentality, cynicism, melodrama and

vulgarity' to be found in Twain, but is it to be found in 'Jim Baker's Blue Jay Yarn'?

'There's more *to* a blue jay than any other creature. He has got more moods, and more different kinds of feelings than other creatures; and, mind you, whatever a blue jay feels, he can put into language. And no mere commonplace language either, but rattling, out-and-out book talk – and bristling with metaphor too – just bristling! And as for command of language – why, *you* never see a blue jay get stuck for a word. No man ever did. They just boil out of him! And another thing: I've noticed a good deal, and there's no bird, or cow, or anything that uses as good grammar as a blue jay. You may say a cat uses good grammar. Well, a cat does – but you let a cat get excited, once; you let a cat get to pulling fur with another cat on a shed, nights, and you'll hear grammar that will give you the lockjaw . . . Now, on top of all this, there's another thing: a jay can out-swear any gentleman in the mines. You think a cat can swear. Well, a cat can; but you give a blue jay a subject that calls for his reserve powers, and where is your cat? Don't talk to *me* – I know too much about this thing.'

Does 'Taming the Bicycle' fit into an 'awful pile of tripe'?

The contrast between [the instructor's] muscles and mine was quite marked. He wanted to test mine, so I offered my biceps – which was my best. It almost made him smile. He said, 'It is pulpy, and soft, and yielding, and rounded; it evades pressure, and glides from under the fingers; in the dark a body might think it was an oyster in a rag.'

If Twain was longing for a spiritual home, it was not for a place too stuffy to appreciate extravagant yet closely-observed empathy with a blue jay or affectionate deprecation of one's own right arm.

But then Pritchett may not have read many of Twain's best short pieces. Only over the last several years have many of them been brought back into circulation. In 1993 Clive James, an-other critic acute and droll, took the occasion of the Library of

America's issuance of two volumes of Twain's 'Tales, Sketches, Speeches and Essays' to observe, in *The New Yorker*, that

You could just about convince yourself that *Huckleberry Finn* was a work of literature in the Old World style, aimed at a refined public – after all, it certainly has the rank, if not the manner. But Twain's journalism is a daunting reminder that he was ready to lavish everything he had on everybody, every time . . . For Twain, there was no division between democracy and creativity. They were versions of the same thing: exuberance.

James however goes on in this review to extol Twain as a paragon of American decency – 'Twain was so blameless that he is likely to make us uncomfortable.' Twain himself was full of discomfort and self-blame. His life may not have been the mess that Pritchett called it, but there was a great deal rotten in America when he flourished, and in his own life fiasco, terror and grief ran high. He was not untouched by the rottenness, and he lived with more than a tortured inkling that much of the grief was his fault. He didn't cherish God, mankind or available polity; if there was anything he had a soft spot for (aside from his wife and daughters, whom he loved and arguably blighted), it was death.

Yet he strove and gloried. Tension finding release at unexpected junctures in sentence after sentence.

'It may be claiming more than a humorist could wish to assert', wrote the aforementioned Howells, 'that he is always in earnest; but this strikes us as the paradoxical charm of [Twain's] best humor. Its wildest extravagance is the break and fling from a deep feeling, a wrath with some folly which disquiets him worse than other men, a personal hatred for some humbug or pretension that embitters him beyond anything but laughter.'

Howells also wrote that Twain 'used English in all its alien derivations as if it were native to his own air, as if it had come up out of American, out of Missourian ground', and that he 'writes English as if it were a primitive and not a derivative language, without Gothic or Latin or Greek behind it, or German or French beside it'.

At any rate his language is intimately his own and yet vigorously extroverted. His spiritual home is on the page, and you can still find him there, pretending perhaps not to be expecting company but in fact relishing it.

I don't know. I'm afraid this introduction is no triumph of form, itself. Probably I should never have looked up *syntonic* and *ego-syntonic* in the dictionary. Once you get away from plain English, you lose track of Mark Twain.

His first biographer, Albert Bigelow Paine, told of finding Twain in bed (where he often wrote), looking for a newspaper clipping. The two of them kept digging around under the covers until finally Twain cried out, 'One could *lose a dog* in this bed!'

Which means, too, that some day, when one least expects it, one might find a dog in there. I suggest that the reader curl up in this collection as though it were such a bed.

ROY BLOUNT JR

Prefatory

If I were to sell the reader a barrel of molasses, and he, instead of sweetening his substantial dinner with the same at judicious intervals, should eat the entire barrel at one sitting, and then abuse me for making him sick, I would say that he deserved to be made sick for not knowing any better how to utilize the blessings this world affords. And if I sell to the reader this volume of nonsense, and he, instead of seasoning his graver reading with a chapter of it now and then, when his mind demands such relaxation, unwisely overdoses himself with several chapters of it at a single sitting, he will well deserve to be nauseated, and he will have nobody to blame but himself if he *is*. There is no more sin in publishing an entire volume of nonsense than there is in keeping a candy store with no hardware in it. It lies wholly with the customer whether he will injure himself by means of either, or will derive from them the benefits which they will afford him if he uses their possibilities judiciously.

Respectfully submitted,

THE AUTHOR

The Celebrated Jumping Frog of Calaveras* County

In compliance with the request of a friend of mine, who wrote me from the East, I called on good-natured, garrulous old Simon Wheeler, and inquired after my friend's friend, *Leonidas W.* Smiley, as requested to do, and I hereunto append the result. I have a lurking suspicion that *Leonidas W.* Smiley is a myth; that my friend never knew such a personage; and that he only conjectured that, if I asked old Wheeler about him, it would remind him of his infamous *Jim* Smiley, and he would go to work and bore me to death with some exasperating reminiscence of him as long and tedious as it should be useless to me. If that was the design, it succeeded.

I found Simon Wheeler dozing comfortably by the bar-room stove of the dilapidated tavern in the decayed mining camp of Angel's, and I noticed that he was fat and bald-headed, and had an expression of winning gentleness and simplicity upon his tranquil countenance. He roused up, and gave me good-day. I told him a friend of mine had commissioned me to make some inquiries about a cherished companion of his boyhood named *Leonidas W.* Smiley – Rev. *Leonidas W.* Smiley, a young minister of the Gospel, who he had heard was at one time a resident of Angel's Camp. I added that, if Mr Wheeler could tell me anything about this Rev. Leonidas W. Smiley, I would feel under many obligations to him.

Simon Wheeler backed me into a corner and blockaded me there with his chair, and then sat down and reeled off the monotonous narrative which follows this paragraph. He never smiled, he never frowned, he never changed his voice from the gentle-flowing key to which he tuned the initial sentence, he never betrayed the slightest suspicion of enthusiasm; but all through the interminable narrative there ran a vein of impressive earnestness and sincerity, which showed me plainly that, so far from his imagining that there was anything ridiculous or funny

* Pronounced Cal-e-*va*-ras.

19

about his story, he regarded it as a really important matter, and admired its two heroes as men of transcendent genius in finesse. I let him go on in his own way, and never interrupted him once.

There was a feller here once by the name of *Jim* Smiley, in the winter of forty-nine – or maybe it was the spring of fifty – I don't recollect exactly, somehow, though what makes me think it was one or the other is because I remember the big flume warn't finished when he first come to the camp; but anyway, he was the curiousest man about always betting on anything that turned up you ever see, if he could get anybody to bet on the other side; and if he couldn't he'd change sides. Anyway what suited the other man would suit him – anyway just so's he got a bet, *he* was satisfied. But still he was lucky, uncommon lucky; he most always come out winner. He was always ready and laying for a chance; there couldn't be no solit'ry thing mentioned but that feller'd offer to bet on it, and take any side you please, as I was just telling you. If there was a horse-race, you'd find him flush or you'd find him busted at the end of it; if there was a dog-fight, he'd bet on it; if there was a cat-fight, he'd bet on it; if there was a chicken-fight, he'd bet on it; why, if there was two birds setting on a fence, he would bet you which one would fly first; or if there was a camp meeting, he would be there reg'lar, to bet on Parson Walker, which he judged to be the best exhorter about here, and so he was too, and a good man. If he even see a straddle-bug start to go anywheres, he would bet you how long it would take him to get to – to wherever he was going to, and if you took him up, he would follow that straddle-bug to Mexico but what he would find out where he was bound for and how long he was on the road. Lots of the boys here has seen that Smiley, and can tell you about him. Why, it never made no difference to *him* – he would bet on *any* thing – the dangdest feller. Parson Walker's wife laid very sick once, for a good while, and it seemed as if they warn't going to save her; but one morning he come in, and Smiley up and asked him how she was, and he said she was considerable better – thank the Lord for his inf'nit mercy – and coming on so smart that with the blessing of Prov'dence she'd get well yet; and Smiley, before he thought, says, 'Well I'll resk two-and-a-half that she don't, anyway.'

Thish-yer Smiley had a mare – the boys called her the fifteen-minute nag, but that was only in fun, you know, because, of course, she was faster than that – and he used to win money on that horse, for all she was so slow and always had the asthma, or the distemper, or the consumption, or something of that kind. They used to give her two or three hundred yards' start, and then pass her under way; but always at the fag-end of the race she'd get excited and desperate-like, and come cavorting and straddling up, and scattering her legs around limber, sometimes in the air, and sometimes out to one side amongst the fences, and kicking up m-o-r-e dust and raising m-o-r-e racket with her coughing and sneezing and blowing her nose – and always fetch up at the stand just about a neck ahead, as near as you could cypher it down.

And he had a little small bull-pup, that to look at him you'd think he warn't worth a cent, but to set around and look ornery, and lay for a chance to steal something. But as soon as money was up on him, he was a different dog; his under-jaw'd begin to stick out like the fo'castle of a steamboat, and his teeth would uncover, and shine wicked, you hear *me*. And a dog might tackle him, and bully-rag him, and bite him, and throw him over his shoulder two or three times, and Andrew Jackson – which was the name of the pup – Andrew Jackson would never let on but what *he* was satisfied, and hadn't expected nothing else – and the bets being doubled and doubled on the other side all the time, till the money was all up; and then all of a sudden he would grab that other dog jest by the j'int of his hind leg and freeze to it – not chaw, you understand, but only jest grip and hang on till they throwed up the sponge, if it was a year. Smiley always come out winner on that pup, till he harnessed a dog once that didn't have no hind legs, because they'd been sawed off by a circular saw, and when the thing had gone along far enough, and the money was all up, and he come to make a snatch for his pet hold, he see in a minute how he'd been imposed on, and how the other dog had him in the door, so to speak, and he 'peared surprised, and then he looked sorter discouraged-like, and didn't try no more to win the fight, and so he got shucked out bad. He give Smiley a look, as much as to say his heart was broke, and it was *his* fault, for putting up a dog that hadn't no hind legs for him to take holt of, which was his main dependence in a fight, and then he limped off a piece and laid down and died. It was a good pup, was that Andrew Jackson, and would have made a name for hisself if he'd lived, for the stuff was in him, and he had genius – I know it, because he hadn't had no opportunities to speak of, and it don't stand to reason that a dog could make such a fight as he could under them circumstances, if he hadn't no talent. It always makes me feel sorry when I think of that last fight of his'n, and the way it turned out.

Well, thish-yer Smiley had rat-tarriers, and chicken cocks, and tom-cats, and all them kind of things, till you couldn't rest, and you couldn't fetch nothing for him to bet on but he'd match you. He ketched a frog one day, and took him home, and said he cal'lated to educate him; and so he never done nothing for three months but set in his back yard and learn that frog to jump. And you bet you he *did* learn him, too. He'd give him a little punch behind, and the next minute you'd see that frog whirling in the air like a doughnut – see him turn one summerset, or maybe a couple, if he got a good start, and come down flat-footed and all right, like a cat. He got him up so in the matter of ketching flies, and kep' him in practice so constant, that he'd nail a fly every time as far as he could see him. Smiley said all a frog wanted was education, and he could do 'most anything – and I believe him. Why, I've seen him set Dan'l Webster down here on this floor – Dan'l Webster was the name of the frog – and sing out, 'Flies, Dan'l, flies!' and quicker'n you could wink, he'd spring straight up, and snake a fly off'n the counter there, and flop down on the floor ag'in as solid as a gob of mud, and fall to scratching the side of his head with his hind foot as indifferent as if he hadn't no idea he'd been doin' any more'n any frog might do. You never see a frog so modest and straightfor'ard as he was, for all he was so gifted. And when it come to fair and square jumping on a dead level, he could get over more ground at one straddle than any animal of his breed you ever see. Jumping on a dead level was his strong suit, you understand; and when it came to that, Smiley would ante up money on him as long as he had a red. Smiley was monstrous proud of his frog, and well he might be, for fellers that had traveled and been everywheres all said he laid over any frog that ever *they* see.

22

Well, Smiley kep' the beast in a little lattice box, and he used to fetch him downtown sometimes and lay for a bet. One day a feller – a stranger in the camp, he was – come acrost him with his box, and says:

'What might it be that you've got in the box?'

And Smiley says, sorter indifferent like, 'It might be a parrot, or it might be a canary, maybe, but it ain't – it's only just a frog.'

And the feller took it, and looked at it careful, and turned it round this way and that, and says, 'H'm – so 'tis. Well, what's *he* good for?'

'Well,' Smiley says, easy and careless, 'he's good enough for *one* thing, I should judge – he can outjump any frog in Calaveras County.'

The feller took the box again, and took another long, particular look, and give it back to Smiley, and says, very deliberate, 'Well, I don't see no p'ints about that frog that's any better'n any other frog.'

'Maybe you don't,' Smiley says. 'Maybe you understand frogs, and maybe you don't understand 'em; maybe you've had experience, and maybe you ain't only a amature, as it were. Anyways, I've got *my* opinion, and I'll resk forty dollars that he can outjump any frog in Calaveras County.'

And the feller studies a minute, and then says, kinder sad-like, 'Well, I'm only a stranger here, and I ain't got no frog; but if I had a frog, I'd bet you.'

And then Smiley says: 'That's all right – that's all right – if you'll hold my box a minute, I'll go and get you a frog.' And so the feller took the box, and put up his forty dollars along with Smiley's, and set down to wait.

So he set there a good while thinking and thinking to himself, and then he got the frog out and prized his mouth open and took a teaspoon and filled him full of quail-shot – filled him pretty near up to his chin – and set him on the floor. Smiley he went to the swamp and slopped around in the mud for a long time, and finally he ketched a frog, and fetched him in, and give him to this feller, and says:

'Now, if you're ready, set him alongside of Dan'l, with his fore-paws just even with Dan'l's, and I'll give the word.' Then he says, 'One – two – three – *git!*' and him and the feller touched up the frogs from behind, and the new frog hopped off lively; but Dan'l give a heave, and hysted up his shoulders – so – like a Frenchman, but it warn't no use – he couldn't budge; he was planted as solid as a church, and he couldn't no more stir than if he was anchored out. Smiley was a good deal surprised, and he was disgusted too, but he didn't have no idea what the matter was, of course.

The feller took the money and started away; and when he was going out at the door, he sorter jerked his thumb over his shoulder – this way – at Dan'l, and says again, very deliberate: 'Well, I don't see no p'ints about that frog that's any better'n any other frog.'

Smiley he stood scratching his head and looking down at Dan'l a long time, and at last he says, 'I do wonder what in the nation that frog throw'd off for – I wonder if there ain't something the matter with him – he 'pears to look mighty baggy, somehow.' And he ketched Dan'l by the nap of the neck, and hefted him, and says, 'Why, blame my cats if he don't weigh five pound!' and turned him upside down, and he belched out a double handful of shot. And then he see how it was, and he was the maddest man – he set the frog down and took out after that feller, but he never ketched him. And—

[Here Simon Wheeler heard his name called from the front yard, and got up to see what was wanted.] And turning to me as he moved away, he said: 'Just set where you are, stranger, and rest easy – I ain't going to be gone a second.'

But, by your leave, I did not think that a continuation of the history of the enterprising vagabond *Jim* Smiley would be likely to afford me much information concerning the Rev. *Leonidas W.* Smiley, and so I started away.

At the door I met the sociable Wheeler returning, and he button-holed me and recommenced:

'Well, thish-yer Smiley had a yaller one-eyed cow that didn't have no tail, only jest a short stump like a bannanner, and—'

Lacking both time and inclination, I did not wait to hear about the afflicted cow, but took my leave.

Concerning Chambermaids

Against all chambermaids, of whatsoever age or nationality, I launch the curse of bachelordom! Because:

They always put the pillows at the opposite end of the bed from the gas-burner, so that while you read and smoke before sleeping (as is the ancient and honored custom of bachelors), you have to hold your book aloft, in an uncomfortable position, to keep the light from dazzling your eyes.

When they find the pillows removed to the other end of the bed in the morning, they receive not the suggestion in a friendly spirit; but, glorying in their absolute sovereignty, and unpitying your helplessness, they make the bed just as it was originally, and gloat in secret over the pang their tyranny will cause you.

Always after that, when they find you have transposed the pillows, they undo your work, and thus defy and seek to embitter the life that God has given you.

If they cannot get the light in an inconvenient position any other way, they move the bed.

If you pull your trunk out six inches from the wall, so that the lid will stay up when you open it, they always shove that trunk back again. They do it on purpose.

If you want the spittoon in a certain spot, where it will be handy, they don't, and so they move it.

They always put your other boots into inaccessible places. They chiefly enjoy depositing them as far under the bed as the wall will permit. It is because this compels you to get down in an undignified attitude and make wild sweeps for them in the dark with the boot-jack, and swear.

They always put the match-box in some other place. They hunt up a new place for it every day, and put up a bottle, or other perishable glass thing, where the box stood before. This is to cause you to break that glass thing, groping in the dark, and get yourself into trouble.

They are for ever and ever moving the furniture. When you come in, in the night, you can calculate on finding the bureau where the wardrobe was in the morning. And when you go out in the morning, if you leave the slop-bucket by the door and rocking-chair by the window, when you come in at midnight, or thereabouts, you will fall over that rocking-chair, and you will proceed toward the window and sit down in that slop-tub. This will disgust you. They like that.

No matter where you put anything, they are not going to let it stay there. They will take it and move it the first chance they get. It is their nature. And, besides, it gives them pleasure to be mean and contrary this way. They would die if they couldn't be villains.

They always save up all the old scraps of printed rubbish you throw on the floor, and stack them up carefully on the table, and start the fire with your valuable manuscripts. If there is any one particular old scrap that you are more down on than any other, and which you are gradually wearing your life out trying to get rid of, you may take all the pains you possibly can in that direction, but it won't be of any use, because they will always fetch that old scrap back and put it in the same old place again every time. It does them good.

And they use up more hair-oil than any six men. If charged with purloining the same, they lie about it. What do they care about a hereafter? Absolutely nothing.

If you leave the key in the door for convenience sake, they will carry it down to the office and give it to the clerk. They do this under the vile pretence of trying to protect your property from thieves; but actually they do it because they want to make you tramp back downstairs after it when you come home tired, or put you to the trouble of sending a waiter for it, which waiter will expect you to pay him something. In which case I suppose the degraded creatures divide.

They keep always trying to make your bed before you get up, thus destroying your rest and inflicting agony upon you; but after you get up, they don't come any more till next day.

They do all the mean things they can think of, and they do them just out of pure cussedness, and nothing else.

Chambermaids are dead to every human instinct.

If I can get a bill through the Legislature abolishing chambermaids, I mean to do it.

Jim Baker's Blue Jay Yarn

Animals talk to each other, of course. There can be no question about that; but I suppose there are very few people who can understand them. I never knew but one man who could. I knew he could, however, because he told me so himself. He was a middle-aged, simple-hearted miner, who had lived in a lonely corner of California, among the woods and mountains, a good many years, and had studied the ways of his only neighbors, the beasts and the birds, until he believed he could accurately translate any remark which they made. This was Jim Baker. According to Jim Baker, some animals have only a limited education and use only very simple words, and scarcely ever a comparison or a flowery figure; whereas, certain other animals have a large vocabulary, a fine command of language, and a ready and fluent delivery; consequently these latter talk a great deal; they like it; they are conscious of their talent, and they enjoy 'showing off'. Baker said that, after long and careful observation, he had come to the conclusion that the blue jays were the best talkers he had found among birds and beasts. Said he:

'There's more to a blue jay than any other creature. He has got more moods and more different kinds of feelings than other creatures; and, mind you, whatever a blue jay feels, he can put into language. And no mere commonplace language either, but rattling, out-and-out book talk – and bristling with metaphor too – just bristling! And as for command of language – why, you never see a blue jay get stuck for a word. No man ever did. They just boil out of him! And another thing: I've noticed a good deal, and there's no bird, or cow, or anything that uses as good grammar as a blue jay. You may say a cat uses good grammar. Well, a cat does – but you let a cat get excited, once; you let a cat get to pulling fur with another cat on a shed, nights, and you'll hear grammar that will give you the lockjaw. Ignorant people think it's the *noise* which fighting cats make that is so aggravating, but it ain't so; it's the sickening grammar they use. Now I've never heard a jay use bad grammar but very seldom;

27

and when they do, they are as ashamed as a human; they shut right down and leave.

'You may call a jay a bird. Well, so he is, in a measure – because he's got feathers on him, and don't belong to no church, perhaps; but otherwise he is just as much a human as you be. And I'll tell you for why. A jay's gifts, and instincts, and feelings, and interests, cover the whole ground. A jay hasn't got any more principle than a Congressman. A jay will lie, a jay will steal, a jay will deceive, a jay will betray; and, four times out of five, a jay will go back on his solemnest promise. The sacredness of an obligation is a thing which you can't cram into no blue jay's head. Now, on top of all this, there's another thing: a jay can out-swear any gentleman in the mines. You think a cat can swear. Well, a cat can; but you give a blue jay a subject that calls for his reserve powers, and where is your cat? Don't talk to *me* – I know too much about this thing. And there's yet another thing: in the one little particular of scolding – just good, clean, out-and-out scolding – a blue jay can lay over anything, human or divine. Yes, sir, a jay is everything that a man is. A jay can cry, a jay can laugh, a jay can feel shame, a jay can reason and plan and discuss, a jay likes gossip and scandal, a jay has got a sense of humor, a jay knows when he is an ass just as well as you do – maybe better. If a jay ain't human, he better take in his sign, that's all. Now I am going to tell you a perfectly true fact about some blue jays.

'When I first begun to understand jay language correctly, there was a little incident happened here. Seven years ago, the last man in this region but me moved away. There stands his house – been empty ever since; a log house, with a plank roof – just one big room, and no more; no ceiling – nothing between the rafters and the floor. Well, one Sunday morning I was sitting out here in front of my cabin, with my cat, taking the sun, and looking at the blue hills, and listening to the leaves rustling so lonely in the trees, and thinking of the home away yonder in the States, that I hadn't heard from in thirteen years, when a blue jay lit on that house, with an acorn in his mouth, and says, "Hallo, I reckon I've struck something!" When he spoke, the acorn fell out of his mouth and rolled down the roof, of course, but he didn't care; his mind was all on the thing he had struck.

It was a knot-hole in the roof. He cocked his head to one side, shut one eye and put the other one to the hole, like a 'possum looking down a jug; then he glanced up with his bright eyes, gave a wink or two with his wings – which signifies gratification, you understand – and says, "It looks like a hole, it's located like a hole – blamed if I don't believe it *is* a hole!"

'Then he cocked his head down and took another look; he glances up perfectly joyful this time; winks his wings and his tail both, and says, "Oh no, this ain't no fat thing, I reckon! If I ain't in luck! – why, it's a perfectly elegant hole!" So he flew down and got that acorn, and fetched it up and dropped it in, and was just tilting his head back with the heavenliest smile on his face, when all of a sudden he was paralyzed into a listening attitude, and that smile faded gradually out of his countenance like breath off'n a razor, and the queerest look of surprise took its place. Then he says, "Why, I didn't hear it fall!" He cocked his eye at the hole again and took a long look; raised up and shook his head; stepped around to the other side of the hole, and took another look from that side; shook his head again. He studied a while, then he just went into the *details* – walked round and round the hole, and spied into it from every point of the compass. No use. Now he took a thinking attitude on the comb of the roof, and scratched the back of his head with his right foot a minute, and finally says, "Well, it's too many for *me*, that's certain; must be a mighty long hole; however, I ain't got no time to fool around here; I got to 'tend to business; I reckon it's all right – chance it, anyway!"

'So he flew off and fetched another acorn and dropped it in, and tried to flirt his eye to the hole quick enough to see what become of it, but he was too late. He held his eye there as much as a minute; then he raised up and sighed, and says, "Confound it, I don't seem to understand this thing, no way; however, I'll tackle her again." He fetched another acorn, and done his level best to see what become of it, but he couldn't. He says, "Well, *I* never struck no such a hole as this before; I'm of the opinion it's a totally new kind of a hole." Then he begun to get mad. He held in for a spell, walking up and down the comb of the roof, and shaking his head and muttering to himself; but his feelings got the upper hand of him presently, and he broke loose and

29

cussed himself black in the face. I never see a bird take on so about a little thing. When he got through, he walks to the hole and looks in again for a half a minute; then he says, "Well, you're a long hole, and a deep hole, and a mighty singular hole altogether – but I've started in to fill you, and I'm d—d if I *don't* fill you, if it takes a hundred years!"

'And with that, away he went. You never see a bird work so since you was born. He laid into his work like a nigger, and the way he hove acorns into that hole for about two hours and a half was one of the most exciting and astonishing spectacles I ever struck. He never stopped to take a look any more – he just hove 'em in, and went for more. Well, at last he could hardly flop his wings, he was so tuckered out. He comes a-drooping down, once more, sweating like an ice-pitcher, drops his acorn in and says, "*Now* I guess I've got the bulge on you by this time!" So he bent down for a look. If you'll believe me, when his head come up again he was just pale with rage. He says, "I've shoveled acorns enough in there to keep the family thirty years, and if I can see a sign of one of 'em, I wish I may land in a museum with a belly full of sawdust in two minutes!"

'He just had strength enough to crawl up onto the comb and lean his back agin the chimbly, and then he collected his impressions and begun to free his mind. I see in a second that what I had mistook for profanity in the mines was only just the rudiments, as you may say.

'Another jay was going by, and heard him doing his devotions, and stops to inquire what was up. The sufferer told him the whole circumstance, and says, "Now yonder's the hole, and if you don't believe me, go and look for yourself." So this fellow went and looked, and comes back and says, "How many did you say you put in there?" "Not any less than two tons," says the sufferer. The other jay went and looked again. He couldn't seem to make it out, so he raised a yell, and three more jays come. They all examined the hole, they all made the sufferer tell it over again, then they all discussed it, and got off as many leatherheaded opinions about it as an average crowd of humans could have done.

'They did call in more jays; then more and more, till pretty soon this whole region 'peared to have a blue flush about it.

There must have been five thousand of them; and such another jawing and disputing and ripping and cussing, you never heard. Every jay in the whole lot put his eye to the hole, and delivered a more chuckle-headed opinion about the mystery than the jay that went there before him. They examined the house all over, too. The door was standing half-open, and at last one old jay happened to go and light on it and look in. Of course, that knocked the mystery galley-west in a second. There lay the acorns, scattered all over the floor. He flopped his wings and raised a whoop. "Come here!" he says; "come here, everybody; hang'd if this fool hasn't been trying to fill up a house with acorns!" They all came a-swooping down like a blue cloud, and as each fellow lit on the door and took a glance, the whole absurdity of the contract that that first jay had tackled hit him home, and he fell over backwards suffocating with laughter, and the next jay took his place and done the same.

'Well, sir, they roosted around here on the house-top and the trees for an hour, and guffawed over that thing like human beings. It ain't no use to tell me a blue jay hasn't got a sense of humor, because I know better. And memory too. They brought jays here from all over the United States to look down that hole, every summer for three years. Other birds too. And they could all see the point, except an owl that come from Nova Scotia to visit the Yo Semite, and he took this thing in on his way back. He said he couldn't see anything funny in it. But then, he was a good deal disappointed about Yo Semite, too.'

A Tramp Abroad

Taming the Bicycle

I thought the matter over, and concluded I could do it. So I went down and bought a barrel of Pond's Extract and a bicycle. The Expert came home with me to instruct me. We chose the back yard, for the sake of privacy, and went to work.

Mine was not a full-grown bicycle, but only a colt – a fifty-inch, with the pedals shortened up to forty-eight – and skittish, like any other colt. The Expert explained the thing's points briefly, then he got on its back and rode around a little, to show me how easy it was to do. He said that the dismounting was perhaps the hardest thing to learn, and so we would leave that to the last. But he was in error there. He found, to his surprise and joy, that all that he needed to do was to get me onto the machine and stand out of the way; I could get off, myself. Although I was wholly inexperienced, I dismounted in the best time on record. He was on that side, shoving up the machine; we all came down with a crash, he at the bottom, I next, and the machine on top.

We examined the machine, but it was not in the least injured. This was hardly believable. Yet the Expert assured me that it was true; in fact, the examination proved it. I was partly to realize, then, how admirably these things are constructed. We applied some Pond's Extract, and resumed. The Expert got on the *other* side to shove up this time, but I dismounted on that side; so the result was as before.

The machine was not hurt. We oiled ourselves up again, and resumed. This time the Expert took up a sheltered position behind, but somehow or other we landed on him again.

He was full of surprised admiration; said it was abnormal. She was all right, not a scratch on her, not a timber started anywhere. I said it was wonderful, while we were greasing up, but he said that when I came to know these steel spider-webs I would realize that nothing but dynamite could cripple them. Then he limped out to position, and we resumed once more. This time the Expert took up the position of short-stop, and got a man to shove up behind. We got up a handsome speed, and presently traversed a brick, and I went out over the top of the tiller and landed, head down, on the instructor's back, and saw the machine fluttering in the air between me and the sun. It was well it came down on us, for that broke the fall, and it was not injured.

Five days later I got out and was carried down to the hospital, and found the Expert doing pretty fairly. In a few more days I was quite sound. I attribute this to my prudence in always dismounting on something soft. Some recommend a feather bed, but I think an Expert is better.

The Expert got out at last, brought four assistants with him. It was a good idea. These four held the graceful cobweb upright while I climbed into the saddle; then they formed in column and marched on either side of me while the Expert pushed behind; all hands assisted at the dismount.

The bicycle had what is called the 'wabbles', and had them very badly. In order to keep my position, a good many things were required of me, and in every instance the thing required was against nature. Against nature, but not against the *laws* of nature. That is to say, that whatever the needed thing might be, my nature, habit, and breeding moved me to attempt it in one way, while some immutable and unsuspected law of physics required that it be done in just the other way. I perceived by this how radically and grotesquely wrong had been the lifelong education of my body and members. They were steeped in ignorance; they knew nothing – nothing which it could profit them to know. For instance, if I found myself falling to the right, I put the tiller hard down the other way, by a quite natural impulse, and so violated a law, and kept on going down. The law required the opposite thing – the big wheel must be turned in the direction in which you are falling. It is hard to believe this, when you are told it. And not merely hard to believe it, but impossible; it is opposed to all your notions. And it is just as hard to do it, after you do come to believe it. Believing it, and knowing by the most convincing proof that it is true, does not help it: you can't any more *do* it than you could before; you can neither force nor persuade yourself to do it at first. The intellect has to come to the front, now. It has to teach the limbs to discard their old education and adopt the new.

The steps of one's progress are distinctly marked. At the end of each lesson he knows he has acquired something, and he also knows what that something is, and likewise that it will stay with him. It is not like studying German, where you mull along, in a groping, uncertain way, for thirty years; and at last, just as you think you've got it, they spring the subjunctive on you, and there you are. No – and I see now, plainly enough, that the great pity about the German language is, that you can't fall off it and hurt yourself. There is nothing like that feature to make you attend strictly to business. But I also see, by what I have learned of bicycling, that the right and only sure way to learn German is by the bicycling method. That is to say, take a grip on one villainy of it at a time, and learn it – not ease up and shirk to the next, leaving that one half learned.

When you have reached the point in bicycling where you can balance the machine tolerably fairly and propel it and steer it, then comes your next task – how to mount it. You do it in this way: you hop along behind it on your right foot, resting the other on the mounting-peg, and grasping the tiller with your hands. At the word, you rise on the peg, stiffen your left leg, hang your other one around in the air in a general and indefinite way, lean your stomach against the rear of the saddle, and then fall off, maybe on one side, maybe on the other; but you fall off. You get up and do it again; and once more; and then several times.

By this time you have learned to keep your balance; and also to steer without wrenching the tiller out by the roots (I say tiller because it *is* a tiller; 'handle-bar' is a lamely descriptive phrase). So you steer along, straight ahead, a little while, then you rise forward, with a steady strain, bringing your right leg, and then your body, into the saddle, catch your breath, fetch a violent hitch this way and then that, and down you go again.

But you have ceased to mind the going down by this time; you are getting to light on one foot or the other with considerable certainty. Six more attempts and six more falls make you perfect. You land in the saddle comfortably, next time, and stay there – that is, if you can be content to let your legs dangle, and leave the pedals alone a while; but if you grab at once for the pedals, you are gone again. You soon learn to wait a little and perfect your balance before reaching for the pedals; then the mounting-art is acquired, is complete, and a little practice will make it simple and easy to you, though spectators ought to keep off a rod or two to one side, along at first, if you have nothing against them.

And now you come to the voluntary dismount; you learned the other kind first of all. It is quite easy to tell one how to do the voluntary dismount; the words are few, the requirement simple, and apparently undifficult; let your left pedal go down till your left leg is nearly straight, turn your wheel to the left, and get off as you would from a horse. It certainly does sound exceedingly easy; but it isn't. I don't know why it isn't, but it isn't. Try as you may, you don't get down as you would from a horse, you get down as you would from a house afire. You make a spectacle of yourself every time.

2

During eight days I took a daily lesson of an hour and a half. At the end of this twelve working-hours' apprenticeship I was graduated – in the rough. I was pronounced competent to paddle my own bicycle without outside help. It seems incredible, this celerity of acquirement. It takes considerably longer than that to learn horseback-riding in the rough.

Now it is true that I could have learned without a teacher, but it would have been risky for me, because of my natural clumsiness. The self-taught man seldom knows anything accurately, and he does not know a tenth as much as he could have known if he had worked under teachers; and, besides, he brags, and is the means of fooling other thoughtless people into going and doing as he himself has done. There are those who imagine that the unlucky accidents of life – life's 'experiences' – are in some way useful to us. I wish I could find out how. I never knew one of them to happen twice. They always change off and swamp around and catch you on your inexperienced side. If personal experience can be worth anything as an education, it wouldn't seem likely that you could trip Methuselah; and yet if that old person could come back here it is more than likely that one of the first things he would do would be to take hold of one of these electric wires and tie himself all up in a knot. Now the surer thing and the wiser thing would be for him to ask some-body whether it was a good thing to take hold of. But that would not suit him; he would be one of the self-taught kind that go by experience; he would want to examine for himself. And he would find, for his instruction, that the coiled patriarch shuns the electric wire; and it would be useful to him, too, and would leave his education in quite a complete and rounded-out condi-tion, till he should come again, some day, and go to bouncing a dynamite-can around to find out what was in it.

But we wander from the point. However, get a teacher; it saves much time and Pond's Extract.

Before taking final leave of me, my instructor inquired con-cerning my physical strength, and I was able to inform him that I hadn't any. He said that that was a defect which would make up-hill wheeling pretty difficult for me at first; but he also said the bicycle would soon remove it. The contrast between his muscles and mine was quite marked. He wanted to test mine, so I offered my biceps – which was my best. It almost made him smile. He said, 'It is pulpy, and soft, and yielding, and rounded; it evades pressure, and glides from under the fingers; in the dark a body might think it was an oyster in a rag.' Perhaps this made me look grieved, for he added, briskly: 'Oh, that's all right; you needn't worry about that; in a little while you can't tell it from a petrified kidney. Just go right along with your practice; you're all right.'

Then he left me, and I started out alone to seek adventures. You don't really have to seek them – that is nothing but a phrase – they come to you.

I chose a reposeful Sabbath-day sort of a back street which was about thirty yards wide between the curbstones. I knew it was not wide enough; still, I thought that by keeping strict watch and wasting no space unnecessarily I could crowd through.

Of course I had trouble mounting the machine, entirely on my own responsibility, with no encouraging moral support from the outside, no sympathetic instructor to say, 'Good! now you're doing well – good again – don't hurry – there, now, you're all right – brace up, go ahead.' In place of this I had some other sup-port. This was a boy, who was perched on a gate-post munching a hunk of maple sugar.

He was full of interest and comment. The first time I failed and went down he said that if he was me he would dress up in pillows, that's what he would do. The next time I went down he advised me to go and learn to ride a tricycle first. The third time I collapsed he said he didn't believe I could stay on a horse-car. But next time I succeeded, and got clumsily under way in a weaving, tottering, uncertain fashion, and occupying pretty much all of the street. My slow and lumbering gait filled the boy to the chin with scorn, and he sung out, 'My, but don't he rip along!' Then he got down from his post and loafed along the sidewalk, still observing and occasionally commenting. Presently he dropped into my wake and followed along behind. A little girl passed by, balancing a wash-board on her head, and giggled, and seemed about to make a remark, but the boy said, rebukingly, 'Let him alone, he's going to a funeral.'

I had been familiar with that street for years, and had always supposed it was a dead level; but it was not, as the bicycle now informed me, to my surprise. The bicycle, in the hands of a novice, is as alert and acute as a spirit-level in the detecting of delicate and vanishing shades of difference in these matters. It notices a rise where your untrained eye would not observe that one existed; it notices any decline which water will run down. I was toiling up a slight rise, but was not aware of it. It made me tug and pant and perspire; and still, labor as I might, the machine came almost to a standstill every little while. At such times the boy would say: 'That's it! take a rest – there ain't no hurry. They can't hold the funeral without *you*.'

Stones were a bother to me. Even the smallest ones gave me a panic when I went over them. I could hit any kind of a stone, no matter how small, if I tried to miss it; and of course at first I couldn't help trying to do that. It is but natural. It is part of the ass that is put in us all, for some inscrutable reason.

I was at the end of my course, at last, and it was necessary for me to round to. This is not a pleasant thing, when you undertake it for the first time on your own responsibility, and neither is it likely to succeed. Your confidence oozes away, you fill steadily up with nameless apprehensions, every fiber of you is tense with a watchful strain, you start a cautious and gradual curve, but your squirmy nerves are all full of electric anxieties, so the curve is quickly demoralized into a jerky and perilous zigzag; then suddenly the nickel-clad horse takes the bit in its mouth and goes slanting for the curbstone, defying all prayers and all your powers to change its mind – your heart stands still, your breath hangs fire, your legs forget to work, straight on you go, and there are but a couple of feet between you and the curb now. And now is the desperate moment, the last chance to save yourself; of course all your instructions fly out of your head, and you whirl your wheel *away* from the curb instead of *toward* it, and so you go sprawling on that granite-bound inhospitable shore. That was my luck; that was my experience. I dragged myself out from under the indestructible bicycle and sat down on the curb to examine.

I started on the return trip. It was now that I saw a farmer's wagon poking along down toward me, loaded with cabbages. If I needed anything to perfect the precariousness of my steering, it was just that. The farmer was occupying the middle of the road with his wagon, leaving barely fourteen or fifteen yards of space on either side. I couldn't shout at him – a beginner can't shout; if he opens his mouth he is gone; he must keep all his attention on his business. But in this grisly emergency, the boy came to the rescue, and for once I had to be grateful to him. He kept a sharp lookout on the swiftly varying impulses and inspirations of my bicycle, and shouted to the man accordingly:

'To the left. Turn to the left, or this jackass'll run over you!' The man started to do it. 'No, to the right, to the right! Hold on! *that* won't do! – to the left! – to the right! – to the *left*! – right! left – ri— Stay where you *are*, or you're a goner!'

And just then I caught the off horse in the starboard and went down in a pile. I said, 'Hang it! Couldn't you *see* I was coming?'

'Yes, I see you was coming, but I couldn't tell which *way* you was coming. Nobody could – now, *could* they? You couldn't yourself – now, *could* you? So what could *I* do?'

There was something in that, and so I had the magnanimity to say so. I said I was no doubt as much to blame as he was.

Within the next five days I achieved so much progress that the boy couldn't keep up with me. He had to go back to his gatepost, and content himself with watching me fall at long range.

There was a row of low stepping-stones across one end of the street, a measured yard apart. Even after I got so I could steer pretty fairly I was so afraid of those stones that I always hit them. They gave me the worst falls I ever got in that street, except those which I got from dogs. I have seen it stated that no expert is quick enough to run over a dog; that a dog is always able to skip out of his way. I think that that may be true: but I think that the reason he couldn't run over the dog was because he was trying to. I did not try to run over any dog. But I ran over every dog that came along. I think it makes a great deal of difference. If you try to run over the dog he knows how to calculate, but if you are trying to miss him he does not know how to calculate, and is liable to jump the wrong way every time. It was always so in my experience. Even when I could not hit a wagon I could hit a dog that came to see me practice. They all liked to see me practice, and they all came, for there was very little going on in our neighborhood to entertain a dog. It took time to learn to miss a dog, but I achieved even that.

I can steer as well as I want to, now, and I will catch that boy out one of these days and run over *him* if he doesn't reform.

Get a bicycle. You will not regret it, if you live.

Fenimore Cooper's Literary Offenses

The Pathfinder and The Deerslayer stand at the head of
Cooper's novels as artistic creations. There are others of
his works which contain parts as perfect as are to be
found in these, and scenes even more thrilling. Not one
can be compared with either of them as a finished
whole.

The defects in both of these tales are comparatively
slight. They were pure works of art.

PROF. LOUNSBURY

The five tales reveal an extraordinary fullness of invention.

... One of the very greatest characters in fiction,
Natty Bumppo ...

The craft of the woodsman, the tricks of the trapper,
all the delicate art of the forest, were familiar to Cooper
from his youth up.

PROF. BRANDER MATTHEWS

Cooper is the greatest artist in the domain of romantic
fiction yet produced by America.

WILKIE COLLINS

It seems to me that it was far from right for the Professor of English Literature in Yale, the Professor of English Literature in
Columbia, and Wilkie Collins to deliver opinions on Cooper's
literature without having read some of it. It would have been
much more decorous to keep silent and let persons talk who
have read Cooper.

Cooper's art has some defects. In one place in Deerslayer, and
in the restricted space of two-thirds of a page, Cooper has scored
114 offenses against literary art out of a possible 115. It breaks
the record.

There are nineteen rules governing literary art in the domain of romantic fiction – some say twenty-two. In *Deerslayer* Cooper violated eighteen of them. These eighteen require:

1. That a tale shall accomplish something and arrive somewhere. But the *Deerslayer* tale accomplishes nothing and arrives in the air.

2. They require that the episodes of a tale shall be necessary parts of the tale, and shall help to develop it. But as the *Deerslayer* tale is not a tale, and accomplishes nothing and arrives nowhere, the episodes have no rightful place in the work, since there was nothing for them to develop.

3. They require that the personages in a tale shall be alive, except in the case of corpses, and that always the reader shall be able to tell the corpses from the others. But this detail has often been overlooked in the *Deerslayer* tale.

4. They require that the personages in a tale, both dead and alive, shall exhibit a sufficient excuse for being there. But this detail also has been overlooked in the *Deerslayer* tale.

5. They require that when the personages of a tale deal in conversation, the talk shall sound like human talk, and be talk such as human beings would be likely to talk in the given circumstances, and have a discoverable meaning, also a discoverable purpose, and a show of relevancy, and remain in the neighborhood of the subject in hand, and be interesting to the reader, and help out the tale, and stop when the people cannot think of anything more to say. But this requirement has been ignored from the beginning of the *Deerslayer* tale to the end of it.

6. They require that when the author describes the character of a personage in his tale, the conduct and conversation of that personage shall justify said description. But this law gets little or no attention in the *Deerslayer* tale, as Natty Bumppo's case will amply prove.

7. They require that when a personage talks like an illustrated, gilt-edged, tree-calf, hand-tooled, seven-dollar Friendship's Offering in the beginning of a paragraph, he shall not talk like a negro minstrel in the end of it. But this rule is flung down and danced upon in the *Deerslayer* tale.

8. They require that crass stupidities shall not be played upon

the reader as 'the craft of the woodsman, the delicate art of the forest', by either the author or the people in the tale. But this rule is persistently violated in the *Deerslayer* tale.

9. They require that the personages of a tale shall confine themselves to possibilities and let miracles alone; or, if they venture a miracle, the author must so plausibly set it forth as to make it look possible and reasonable. But these rules are not respected in the *Deerslayer* tale.

10. They require that the author shall make the reader feel a deep interest in the personages of his tale and in their fate; and that he shall make the reader love the good people in the tale and hate the bad ones. But the reader of the *Deerslayer* tale dislikes the good people in it, is indifferent to the others, and wishes they would all get drowned together.

11. They require that the characters in a tale shall be so clearly defined that the reader can tell beforehand what each will do in a given emergency. But in the *Deerslayer* tale this rule is vacated.

In addition to these large rules there are some little ones. These require that the author shall

12. *Say* what he is proposing to say, not merely come near it.

13. Use the right word, not its second cousin.

14. Eschew surplusage.

15. Not omit necessary details.

16. Avoid slovenliness of form.

17. Use good grammar.

18. Employ a simple and straightforward style.

Even these seven are coldly and persistently violated in the *Deerslayer* tale.

Cooper's gift in the way of invention was not a rich endowment; but such as it was he liked to work it, he was pleased with the effects, and indeed he did some quite sweet things with it. In his little box of stage-properties he kept six or eight cunning devices, tricks, artifices for his savages and woodsmen to deceive and circumvent each other with, and he was never so happy as when he was working these innocent things and seeing them go. A favorite one was to make a moccasined person tread in the tracks of the moccasined enemy, and thus hide his own trail. Cooper wore out barrels and barrels of moccasins in working that trick. Another stage-property that he pulled out of his box pretty frequently was his broken twig. He prized his broken twig above all the rest of his effects, and worked it the hardest. It is a restful chapter in any book of his when somebody doesn't step on a dry twig and alarm all the reds and whites for two hundred yards around. Every time a Cooper person is in peril, and absolute silence is worth four dollars a minute, he is sure to step on a dry twig. There may be a hundred handier things to step on, but that wouldn't satisfy Cooper. Cooper requires him to turn out and find a dry twig; and if he can't do it, go and borrow one. In fact, the Leatherstocking Series ought to have been called the Broken Twig Series.

I am sorry there is not room to put in a few dozen instances of the delicate art of the forest, as practiced by Natty Bumppo and some of the other Cooperian experts. Perhaps we may venture two or three samples. Cooper was a sailor – a naval officer; yet he gravely tells us how a vessel, driving toward a lee shore in a gale, is steered for a particular spot by her skipper because he knows of an *undertow* there which will hold her back against the gale and save her. For just pure woodcraft, or sailorcraft, or whatever it is, isn't that neat? For several years Cooper was daily in the society of artillery, and he ought to have noticed that when a cannon-ball strikes the ground it either buries itself or skips a hundred feet or so; skips again a hundred feet or so – and so on, till finally it gets tired and rolls. Now in one place he loses some 'females' – as he always calls women – in the edge of a wood near a plain at night in a fog, on purpose to give Bumppo a chance to show off the delicate art of the forest before the reader. These mislaid people are hunting for a fort. They hear a cannon-blast, and a cannon-ball presently comes rolling into the wood and stops at their feet. To the females this suggests nothing. The case is very different with the admirable Bumppo. I wish I may never know peace again if he doesn't strike out promptly and *follow the track* of that cannon-ball across the plain through the dense fog and find the fort. Isn't it a daisy? If Cooper had any real knowledge of Nature's ways of doing things, he had a most delicate art in concealing the fact. For instance: one of his acute Indian experts, Chingachgook (pronounced Chicago, I think), has lost the trail of a person he is

43

tracking through the forest. Apparently that trail is hopelessly lost. Neither you nor I could ever have guessed out the way to find it. It was very different with Chicago. Chicago was not stumped for long. He turned a running stream out of its course, and there, in the slush in its old bed, were that person's moccasin tracks. The current did not wash them away, as it would have done in all other like cases – no, even the eternal laws of Nature have to vacate when Cooper wants to put up a delicate job of woodcraft on the reader.

We must be a little wary when Brander Matthews tell us that Cooper's books 'reveal an extraordinary fullness of invention'. As a rule, I am quite willing to accept Brander Matthews's literary judgments and applaud his lucid and graceful phrasing of them; but that particular statement needs to be taken with a few tons of salt. Bless your heart, Cooper hadn't any more invention than a horse; and I don't mean a high-class horse, either; I mean a clothes-horse. It would be very difficult to find a really clever 'situation' in Cooper' books, and still more difficult to find one of any kind which he has failed to render absurd by his handling of it. Look at the episodes of 'the caves'; and at the celebrated scuffle between Maqua and those others on the table-land a few days later; and at Hurry Harry's queer water-transit from the castle to the ark; and at Deerslayer's half-hour with his first corpse; and at the quarrel between Hurry Harry and Deerslayer later; and at – but choose for yourself; you can't go amiss.

If Cooper had been an observer his inventive faculty would have worked better; not more interestingly, but more rationally, more plausibly. Cooper's proudest creations in the way of 'situations' suffer noticeably from the absence of the observer's protecting gift. Cooper's eye was splendidly inaccurate. Cooper seldom saw anything correctly. He saw nearly all things as through a glass eye, darkly. Of course a man who cannot see the commonest little everyday matters accurately is working at a disadvantage when he is constructing a 'situation'. In the *Deerslayer* tale Cooper has a stream which is fifty feet wide where it flows out of a lake; it presently narrows to twenty as it meanders along for no given reason, and yet when a stream acts like that it ought to be required to explain itself. Fourteen pages later the width of the brook's outlet from the lake has suddenly shrunk

44

thirty feet, and become 'the narrowest part of the stream'. This shrinkage is not accounted for. The stream has bends in it, a sure indication that it has alluvial banks and cuts them; yet these bends are only thirty and fifty feet long. If Cooper had been a nice and punctilious observer he would have noticed that the bends were oftener nine hundred feet long than short of it.

Cooper made the exit of that stream fifty feet wide, in the first place, for no particular reason; in the second place, he narrowed it to less than twenty to accommodate some Indians. He bends a 'sapling' to the form of an arch over this narrow passage, and conceals six Indians in its foliage. They are 'laying' for a settler's scow or ark which is coming up the stream on its way to the lake; it is being hauled against the stiff current by a rope whose stationary end is anchored in the lake; its rate of progress cannot be more than a mile an hour. Cooper describes the ark, but pretty obscurely. In the matter of dimensions 'it was little more than a modern canal-boat'. Let us guess, then, that it was about one hundred and forty feet long. It was of 'greater breadth than common'. Let us guess, then, that it was about sixteen feet wide. This leviathan had been prowling down bends which were but a third as long as itself, and scraping between banks where it had only two feet of space to spare on each side. We cannot too much admire this miracle. A low-roofed log dwelling occupies 'two-thirds of the ark's length' – a dwelling ninety feet long and sixteen feet wide, let us say – a kind of vestibule train. The dwelling has two rooms – each forty-five feet long and sixteen feet wide, let us guess. One of them is the bedroom of the Hutter girls, Judith and Hetty; the other is the parlor in the daytime, at night it is papa's bedchamber. The ark is arriving at the stream's exit now, whose width has been reduced to less than twenty feet to accommodate the Indians – say to eighteen. There is a foot to spare on each side of the boat. Did the Indians notice that there was going to be a tight squeeze there? Did they notice that they could make money by climbing down out of that arched sapling and just stepping aboard when the ark scraped by? No, other Indians would have noticed these things, but Cooper's Indians never notice anything. Cooper thinks they are marvelous creatures for noticing, but he was almost always in error about his

45

Indians. There was seldom a sane one among them.

The ark is one hundred and forty feet long; the dwelling is ninety feet long. The idea of the Indians is to drop softly and secretly from the arched sapling to the dwelling as the ark creeps along under it at the rate of a mile an hour, and butcher the family. It will take the ark a minute and a half to pass under. It will take the ninety-foot dwelling a minute to pass under. Now, then, what did the six Indians do? It would take you thirty years to guess, and even then you would have to give it up, I believe. Therefore, I will tell you what the Indians did. Their chief, a person of quite extraordinary intellect for a Cooper Indian, warily watched the canal-boat as it squeezed along under him, and when he had got his calculations fined down to exactly the right shade, as he judged, he let go and dropped. And *missed the house*! That is actually what he did. He missed the house, and landed in the stern of the scow. It was not much of a fall, yet it knocked him silly. He lay there unconscious. If the house had been ninety-seven feet long he would have made the trip. The fault was Cooper's, not his. The error lay in the construction of the house. Cooper was no architect.

There still remained in the roost five Indians. The boat has passed under and is now out of their reach. Let me explain what the five did – you would not be able to reason it out for yourself. No. 1 jumped for the boat, but fell in the water astern of it. Then No. 2 jumped for the boat, but fell in the water still further astern of it. Then No. 3 jumped for the boat, and fell a good way astern of it. Then No. 4 jumped for the boat, and fell in the water *away* astern. Then even No. 5 made a jump for the boat – for he was a Cooper Indian. In the matter of intellect, the difference between a Cooper Indian and the Indian that stands in front of the cigar-shop is not spacious. The scow episode is really a sublime burst of invention; but it does not thrill, because the inaccuracy of the details throws a sort of air of fictitiousness and general improbability over it. This comes of Cooper's inadequacy as an observer.

The reader will find some examples of Cooper's high talent for inaccurate observation in the account of the shooting-match in *The Pathfinder*: 'A common wrought nail was driven lightly into the target, its head having been first touched with paint.' The color of the paint is not stated – an important omission, but Cooper deals freely in important omissions. No, after all, it was not an important omission; for this nail-head is *a hundred yards* from the marksmen, and could not be seen by them at that distance, no matter what its color might be. How far can the best eyes see a common house-fly? A hundred yards? It is quite impossible. Very well; eyes that cannot see a house-fly that is a hundred yards away cannot see an ordinary nail-head at that distance, for the size of the two objects is the same. It takes a keen eye to see a fly or a nail-head at fifty yards – one hundred and fifty feet. Can the reader do it?

The nail was lightly driven, its head painted, and game called. Then the Cooper miracles began. The bullet of the first marksman chipped an edge of the nail-head; the next man's bullet drove the nail a little way into the target – and removed all the paint. Haven't the miracles gone far enough now? Not to suit Cooper; for the purpose of this whole scheme is to show off his prodigy, Deerslayer-Hawkeye-Long-Rifle-Leatherstocking-Pathfinder-Bumppo before the ladies.

'Be all ready to clench it, boys!' cried out Pathfinder, stepping into his friend's tracks the instant they were vacant. 'Never mind a new nail; I can see that, though the paint is gone, and what I can see I can hit at a hundred yards, though it were only a mosquito's eye. Be ready to clench!'

The rifle cracked, the bullet sped its way, and the head of the nail was buried in the wood, covered by the piece of flattened lead.

There, you see, is a man who could hunt flies with a rifle, and command a ducal salary in a Wild West show today if we had him back with us.

The recorded feat is certainly surprising just as it stands; but it is not surprising enough for Cooper. Cooper adds a touch. He has made Pathfinder do this miracle with another man's rifle; and not only that but Pathfinder did not have even the advantage of loading it himself. He had everything against him, and yet he made that impossible shot, and not only made it, but did it with absolute confidence, saying 'Be ready to clench.' Now a person like that would have undertaken that same feat with a brickbat, and with Cooper to help he would have achieved it, too.

Pathfinder showed off handsomely that day before the ladies. His very first feat a thing which no Wild West show can touch. He was standing with the group of marksmen, observing – a hundred yards from the target, mind; one Jasper raised his rifle and drove the center of the bull's-eye. Then the Quartermaster fired. The target exhibited no result this time. There was a laugh. 'It's a dead miss,' said Major Lundie. Pathfinder waited an impressive moment or two; then said, in that calm, indifferent, know-it-all way of his, 'No, Major, he has covered Jasper's bullet, as will be seen if anyone will take the trouble to examine the target.'

Wasn't it remarkable! How *could* he see that little pellet fly through the air and enter that distant bullet-hole? Yet that is what he did; for nothing is impossible to a Cooper person. Did any of those people have any deep-seated doubts about this thing? No; for that would imply sanity, and these were all Cooper people. 'The respect for Pathfinder's skill and for his *quickness and accuracy of sight* [the italics are mine] was so profound and general, that the instant he made this declaration the spectators began to distrust their own opinions, and a dozen rushed to the target in order to ascertain the fact. There, sure enough, it was found that the Quartermaster's bullet had gone through the hole made by Jasper's, and that, too, so accurately as to require a minute examination to be certain of the circumstance, which, however, was soon clearly established by discovering one bullet over the other in the stump against which the target was placed.'

They made a 'minute' examination; but never mind, how could they know that there were two bullets in that hole without digging the latest one out? for neither probe nor eyesight could prove the presence of any more than one bullet. Did they dig? No; as we shall see. It is the Pathfinder's turn now; he steps out before the ladies, takes aim, and fires.

But, alas! here is a disappointment; an incredible, an unimaginable disappointment – for the target's aspect is unchanged; there is nothing there but that same old bullet-hole!

'If one dared to hint at such a thing,' cried Major Duncan, 'I should say that the Pathfinder has also missed the target!'

As nobody had missed it yet, the 'also' was not necessary; but never mind about that, for the Pathfinder is going to speak.

'No, no, Major,' said he, confidently, 'that *would* be a risky declaration. I didn't load the piece, and can't say what was in it; but if it was lead, you will find the bullet driving down those of the Quartermaster and Jasper, else is not my name Pathfinder.'

A shout from the target announced the truth of this assertion.

Is the miracle sufficient as it stands? Not for Cooper. The Pathfinder speaks again, as he 'now slowly advances toward the stage occupied by the females':

'That's not all, boys, that's not all; if you find the target touched at all, I'll own to a miss. The Quartermaster cut the wood, but you'll find no wood cut by that last messenger.'

The miracle is at last complete. He knew – doubtless *saw* – at the distance of a hundred yards – that his bullet had passed into the hole *without fraying the edges*. There were now three bullets in that one hole – three bullets embedded processionally in the body of the stump back of the target. Everybody knew this – somehow or other – and yet nobody had dug any of them out to make sure. Cooper is not a close observer, but he is interesting. He is certainly always that, no matter what happens. And he is more interesting when he is not noticing what he is about than when he is. This is a considerable merit.

The conversations in the Cooper books have a curious sound in our modern ears. To believe that such talk really ever came out of people's mouths would be to believe that there was a time when time was of no value to a person who thought he had something to say; when it was the custom to spread a two-minute remark out to ten; when a man's mouth was a rolling-mill, and busied itself all day long in turning four-foot pigs of thought into thirty-foot bars of conversational railroad iron by attenuation; when subjects were seldom faithfully stuck to, but the talk wandered all around and arrived nowhere; when conversations consisted mainly of irrelevancies, with here and there a relevancy, a relevancy with an embarrassed

49

look, as not being able to explain how it got there.

Cooper was certainly not a master in the construction of dialogue. Inaccurate observation defeated him here as it defeated him in so many other enterprises of his. He even failed to notice that the man who talks corrupt English six days in the week must and will talk it on the seventh, and can't help himself. In the *Deerslayer* story he lets Deerslayer talk the showiest kind of book-talk sometimes, and at other times the basest of base dialects. For instance, when someone asks him if he has a sweetheart, and if so, where she abides, this is his majestic answer:

'She's in the forest – hanging from the boughs of the trees, in a soft rain – in the dew on the open grass – the clouds that float about in the blue heavens – the birds that sing in the woods – the sweet springs where I slake my thirst – and in all the other glorious gifts that come from God's Providence!'

And he preceded that, a little before, with this:

'It consarns me as all things that touches a fri'nd consarns a fri'nd.'

And this is another of his remarks:

'If I was Injin born, now, I might tell of this, or carry in the scalp and boast of the expl'ite afore the whole tribe; or if my inimy had only been a bear' – [and so on].

We cannot imagine such a thing as a veteran Scotch Commander-in-Chief comporting himself in the field like a windy melodramatic actor, but Cooper could. On one occasion Alice and Cora were being chased by the French through a fog in the neighborhood of their father's fort:

'*Point de quartier aux coquins!*' cried an eager pursuer, who seemed to direct the operations of the enemy.
'Stand firm and be ready, my gallant 60ths!' suddenly exclaimed a voice above them; 'wait to see the enemy; fire low, and sweep the glacis.'

'Father! father,' exclaimed a piercing cry from out the mist, 'it is I! Alice! thy own Elsie! spare, O! save your daughters!'

'Hold!' shouted the former speaker, in the awful tones of parental agony, the sound reaching even to the woods, and rolling back in solemn echo. ' 'Tis she! God has restored me my children! Throw open the sally-port; to the field, 60ths, to the field! pull not a trigger, lest ye kill my lambs! Drive off these dogs of France with your steel!'

Cooper's word-sense was singularly dull. When a person has a poor ear for music he will flat and sharp right along without knowing it. He keeps near the tune, but it is *not* the tune. When a person has a poor ear for words, the result is a literary flatting and sharping; you perceive what he is intending to say, but you also perceive that he doesn't *say* it. This is Cooper. He was not a word-musician. His ear was satisfied with the *approximate* word. I will furnish some circumstantial evidence in support of this charge. My instances are gathered from half a dozen pages of the tale called *Deerslayer*. He uses 'verbal' for 'oral'; 'precision' for 'facility'; 'phenomena' for 'marvels'; 'necessary' for 'predetermined'; 'unsophisticated' for 'primitive'; 'preparation' for 'expectancy'; 'rebuked' for 'subdued'; 'dependent on' for 'resulting from'; 'fact' for 'condition'; 'fact' for 'conjecture'; 'precaution' for 'caution'; 'explain' for 'determine'; 'mortified' for 'disappointed'; 'meretricious' for 'factitious'; 'materially' for 'considerably'; 'decreasing' for 'deepening'; 'increasing' for 'disappearing'; 'embedded' for 'inclosed'; 'treacherous' for 'hostile'; 'stood' for 'stooped'; 'softened' for 'replaced'; 'rejoined' for 'remarked'; 'situation' for 'condition'; 'different' for 'differing'; 'insensible' for 'unsentient'; 'brevity' for 'celerity'; 'distrusted' for 'suspicious'; 'mental imbecility' for 'imbecility'; 'eyes' for 'sight'; 'counteracting' for 'opposing'; 'funeral obsequies' for 'obsequies'.

There have been daring people in the world who claimed that Cooper could write English, but they are all dead now – all dead but Lounsbury. I don't remember that Lounsbury makes the claim in so many words, still he makes it, for he says that *Deerslayer* is a 'pure work of art'. Pure, in that connection, means faultless – faultless in all details – and language is a detail. If Mr Lounsbury had only compared Cooper's English with the

English which he writes himself – but it is plain that he didn't; and so it is likely that he imagines until this day that Cooper's is as clean and compact as his own. Now I feel sure, deep down in my heart, that Cooper wrote about the poorest English that exists in our language, and that the English of *Deerslayer* is the very worst that even Cooper ever wrote.

I may be mistaken, but it does seem to me that *Deerslayer* is not a work of art in any sense; it does seem to me that it is destitute of every detail that goes to the making of a work of art; in truth, it seems to me that *Deerslayer* is just simply a literary delirium tremens.

A work of art? It has no invention; it has no order, system, sequences or result; it has no lifelikeness, no thrill, no stir, no seeming of reality; its characters are confusedly drawn, and by their acts and words they prove that they are not the sort of people the author claims that they are; its humor is pathetic; its pathos is funny; its conversations are – oh! indescribable; its love-scenes odious; its English a crime against the language.

Counting these out, what is left is Art. I think we must all admit that.

Journalism in Tennessee

The editor of the Memphis *Avalanche* swoops thus mildly down upon a correspondent who posted him as a Radical: 'While he was writing the first word, the middle, dotting his i's, crossing his t's and punching his period, he knew he was concocting a sentence that was saturated with infamy and reeking with falsehood.'

Exchange

I was told by the physician that a Southern climate would improve my health, and so I went down to Tennessee, and got a berth on the *Morning Glory and Johnson County War-Whoop* as associate editor. When I went on duty I found the chief editor sitting tilted back in a three-legged chair with his feet on a pine table. There was another pine table in the room and another afflicted chair, and both were half buried under newspapers and scraps and sheets of manuscript. There was a wooden box of sand, sprinkled with cigar stubs and 'old soldiers', and a stove with a door hanging by its upper hinge. The chief editor had a long-tailed black cloth frock coat on, and white linen pants. His boots were small and neatly blacked. He wore a ruffled shirt, a large seal ring, a standing collar of obsolete pattern, and a checkered neckerchief with the ends hanging down. Date of costume about 1848. He was smoking a cigar, and trying to think of a word, and in pawing his hair he had rumpled his locks a good deal. He was scowling fearfully, and I judged that he was concocting a particularly knotty editorial. He told me to take the exchanges and skim through them and write up the 'Spirit of the Tennessee Press', condensing into the article all of their contents that seemed of interest.

I wrote as follows:

SPIRIT OF THE TENNESSEE PRESS

The editors of the *Semi-Weekly Earthquake* evidently labor under a misapprehension with regard to the Ballyhack railroad. It is not the object of the company to leave Buzzardville off to one side. On the contrary, they consider it one of the most important points along the line, and consequently can have no desire to slight it. The gentlemen of the *Earthquake* will, of course, take pleasure in making the correction.

John W. Blossom, Esq., the able editor of the Higginsville *Thunderbolt and Battle Cry of Freedom*, arrived in the city yesterday. He is stopping at the Van Buren House.

We observe that our contemporary of the Mud Springs *Morning Howl* has fallen into the error of supposing that the election of Van Werter is not an established fact, but he will have discovered his mistake before this reminder reaches him, no doubt. He was doubtless misled by incomplete election returns.

It is pleasant to note that the city of Blathersville is endeavoring to contract with some New York gentlemen to pave its well-nigh impassable streets with the Nicholson pavement. The *Daily Hurrah* urges the measure with ability, and seems confident of ultimate success.

I passed my manuscript over to the chief editor for acceptance, alteration, or destruction. He glanced at it and his face clouded. He ran his eye down the pages, and his countenance grew portentous. It was easy to see that something was wrong. Presently he sprang up and said –

'Thunder and lightning! Do you suppose I am going to speak of those cattle that way? Do you suppose my subscribers are going to stand such gruel as that? Give me the pen!'

I never saw a pen scrape and scratch its way so viciously, or plow through another man's verbs and adjectives so relentlessly. While he was in the midst of his work, somebody shot at him through the open window, and marred the symmetry of my ear.

'Ah,' said he, 'that is that scoundrel Smith, of the *Moral Volcano* – he was due yesterday.' And he snatched a navy revolver from his belt and fired. Smith dropped, shot in the thigh. The shot spoiled Smith's aim, who was just taking a second chance, and he crippled a stranger. It was me. Merely a finger shot off.

Then the chief editor went on with his erasures and interlineations. Just as he finished them a hand grenade came down the stovepipe, and the explosion shivered the stove into a thousand fragments. However, it did no further damage, except that a vagrant piece knocked a couple of my teeth out.

'That stove is utterly ruined,' said the chief editor.

I said I believed it was.

'Well, no matter – don't want it this kind of weather. I know the man that did it. I'll get him. Now, *here* is the way this stuff ought to be written.'

I took the manuscript. It was scarred with erasures and interlineations till its mother wouldn't have known it if it had had one. It now read as follows:

SPIRIT OF THE TENNESSEE PRESS

The inveterate liars of the *Semi-Weekly Earthquake* are evidently endeavoring to palm off upon a noble and chivalrous people another of their vile and brutal falsehoods with regard to that most glorious conception of the nineteenth century, the Ballyhack railroad. The idea that Buzzardville was to be left off at one side originated in their own fulsome brains – or rather in the settlings which *they* regard as brains. They had better swallow this lie if they want to save their abandoned reptile carcasses the cowhiding they so richly deserve.

That ass, Blossom, of the Higginsville *Thunderbolt and Battle Cry of Freedom*, is down here again sponging at the Van Buren.

We observe that the besotted blackguard of the Mud Springs *Morning Howl* is giving out, with his usual propensity for lying, that Van Werter is not elected. The heaven-born mission of journalism is to disseminate truth; to eradicate error; to educate, refine, and elevate the tone of public morals and manners, and make all men more gentle, more virtuous, more charitable, and in all ways better, and holier, and happier; and yet this blackhearted scoundrel degrades his great office persistently to the dissemination of falsehood, calumny, vituperation, and vulgarity.

Blathersville wants a Nicholson pavement – it wants a jail and a poorhouse more. The idea of a pavement in a one horse town composed of two gin mills, a blacksmith's shop, and that mustard plaster of a newspaper, the *Daily Hurrah*! The crawling insect, Buckner, who edits the *Hurrah*, is braying about this business with his customary imbecility, and imagining that he is talking sense.

'Now *that* is the way to write – peppery and to the point. Mush-and-milk journalism gives me the fan-tods.'

About this time a brick came through the window with a splintering crash, and gave me a considerable of a jolt in the back. I moved out of range – I began to feel in the way.

The chief said, 'That was the Colonel, likely. I've been expecting him for two days. He will be up, now, right away.'

He was correct. The Colonel appeared in the door a moment afterward with a dragoon revolver in his hand.

He said, 'Sir, have I the honor of addressing the poltroon who edits this mangy sheet?'

'You have. Be seated, sir. Be careful of the chair, one of its legs is gone. I believe I have the honor of addressing the putrid liar, Col. Blatherskite Tecumseh?'

'Right, sir. I have a little account to settle with you. If you are at leisure we will begin.'

'I have an article on the "Encouraging Progress of Moral and Intellectual Development in America" to finish, but there is no hurry. Begin.'

Both pistols rang out their fierce clamor at the same instant. The chief lost a lock of his hair, and the Colonel's bullet ended its career in the fleshy part of my thigh. The Colonel's left shoulder was clipped a little. They fired again. Both missed their men this time, but I got my share, a shot in the arm. At the third fire both gentlemen were wounded slightly, and I had a knuckle chipped. I then said, I believed I would go out and take a walk, as this was a private matter, and I had a delicacy about participating in it further. But both gentlemen begged me to keep my seat, and assured me that I was not in the way.

They then talked about the elections and the crops while they reloaded, and I fell to tying up my wounds. But presently they opened fire again with animation, and every shot took effect – but it is proper to remark that five out of the six fell to my share. The sixth one mortally wounded the Colonel, who remarked, with fine humor, that he would have to say good morning now, as he had business uptown. He then inquired the way to the undertaker's and left.

The chief turned to me and said, 'I am expecting company to dinner, and shall have to get ready. It will be a favor to me if you will read proof and attend to the customers.'

I winced a little at the idea of attending to the customers, but I was too bewildered by the fusillade that was still ringing in my ears to think of anything to say.

He continued, 'Jones will be here at three – cowhide him. Gillespie will call earlier, perhaps – throw him out of the window. Ferguson will be along about four – kill him. That is all for today, I believe. If you have any odd time, you may write a blistering article on the police – give the Chief Inspector rats. The cowhides are under the table; weapons in the drawer – ammunition there in the corner – lint and bandages up there in the pigeon-holes. In case of accident, go to Lancet, the surgeon, downstairs. He advertises – we take it out in trade.'

He was gone. I shuddered. At the end of the next three hours I had been through perils so awful that all peace of mind and all cheerfulness were gone from me. Gillespie had called and thrown *me* out of the window. Jones arrived promptly, and when I got ready to do the cowhiding he took the job off my hands. In an encounter with a stranger, not in the bill of fare, I had lost my scalp. Another stranger, by the name of Thompson, left me a mere wreck and ruin of chaotic rags. And at last, at bay in the corner, and beset by an infuriated mob of editors, blacklegs, politicians, and desperadoes, who raved and swore and flourished their weapons about my head till the air shimmered with glancing flashes of steel, I was in the act of resigning my berth on the paper when the chief arrived, and with him a rabble of charmed and enthusiastic friends. Then ensued a scene of riot and carnage such as no human pen, or steel one either, could describe. People were shot, probed, dismembered, blown up, thrown out of the window. There was a brief tornado of murky blasphemy, with a confused and frantic war-dance glimmering through it, and then all was over. In five minutes there was silence, and the gory chief and I sat alone and surveyed the sanguinary ruin that strewed the floor around us.

He said, 'You'll like this place when you get used to it.'

I said, 'I'll have to get you to excuse me; I think maybe I might write to suit you after a while; as soon as I had had some practice and learned the language I am confident I could. But, to speak the plain truth, that sort of energy of expression has its inconveniences and a man is liable to interruption. You see that yourself. Vigorous writing is calculated to elevate the public, no doubt, but then I do not like to attract so much attention as it calls forth. I can't write with comfort when I am interrupted so much as I have been today. I like this berth well enough, but I don't like to be left here to wait on the customers. The experiences are novel, I grant you, and entertaining too, after a fashion, but they are not judiciously distributed. A gentleman shoots at you through the window and cripples *me*; a bomb-shell comes down the stovepipe for your gratification and sends the stove-door down *my* throat; a friend drops in to swap compliments with you, and freckles *me* with bullet-holes till my skin won't hold my principles; you go to dinner and Jones comes in with his cowhide, Gillespie throws me out of the window, Thompson tears all my clothes off, and an entire stranger takes my scalp with the easy freedom of an old acquaintance; and in less than five minutes all the blackguards in the country arrive in their war-paint, and proceed to scare the rest of me to death with their tomahawks. Take it altogether, I never had such a spirited time in all my life as I have had today. No; I like you, and I like your calm unruffled way of explaining things to the customers, but you see I am not used to it. The Southern heart is too impulsive; Southern hospitality is too lavish with the stranger. The paragraphs which I have written today, and into whose cold sentences your masterly hand has infused the fervent spirit of Tennessean journalism, will wake up another nest of hornets. All that mob of editors will come – and they will come hungry, too, and want somebody for breakfast. I shall have to bid you adieu. I decline to be present at these festivities. I came South for my health, I will go back on the same errand, and suddenly. Tennessean journalism is too stirring for me.'

After which we parted with mutual regret, and I took apartments at the hospital.

/

A Touching Story of George Washington's Boyhood

If it please your neighbor to break the sacred calm of night with the snorting of an unholy trombone, it is your duty to put up with his wretched music and your privilege to pity him for the unhappy instinct that moves him to delight in such discordant sounds. I did not always think thus: this consideration for musical amateurs was born of certain disagreeable personal experiences that once followed the development of a like instinct in myself. Now this infidel over the way, who is learning to play on the trombone, and the slowness of whose progress is almost miraculous, goes on with his harrowing work every night, uncursed by me, but tenderly pitied. Ten years ago, for the same offense, I would have set fire to his house. At that time I was a prey to an amateur violinist for two or three weeks, and the sufferings I endured at his hands are inconceivable. He played 'Old Dan Tucker', and he never played anything else; but he performed that so badly that he could throw me into fits with it if I were awake, or into a nightmare if I were asleep. As long as he confined himself to 'Dan Tucker', though, I bore with him and abstained from violence; but when he projected a fresh outrage, and tried to do 'Sweet Home', I went over and burnt him out. My next assailant was a wretch who felt a call to play the clarionet. He only played the scale, however, with his distressing instrument, and I let him run the length of his tether, also; but finally, when he branched out into a ghastly tune, I felt my reason deserting me under the exquisite torture, and I sallied forth and burnt him out likewise. During the next two years I burned out an amateur cornet player, a bugler, a bassoon-sophomore, and a barbarian whose talents ran in the bass-drum line.

I would certainly have scorched this trombone man if he had moved into my neighborhood in those days. But as I said before, I leave him to his own destruction now, because I have had experience as an amateur myself, and I feel nothing but compassion for that kind of people. Besides, I have learned that there lies dormant in the souls of all men a penchant for some particular musical instrument, and an unsuspected yearning to learn to play on it, that are bound to wake up and demand attention some day. Therefore, you who rail at such as disturb your slumbers with unsuccessful and demoralizing attempts to subjugate a fiddle, beware! for sooner or later your own time will come. It is customary and popular to curse these amateurs when they wrench you out of a pleasant dream at night with a peculiarly diabolical note; but seeing that we are all made alike, and must all develop a distorted talent for music in the fullness of time, it is not right. I am charitable to my trombone maniac; in a moment of inspiration he fetches a snort, sometimes, that brings me to a sitting posture in bed, broad awake and weltering in a cold perspiration. Perhaps my first thought is, that there has been an earthquake; perhaps I hear the trombone, and my next thought is, that suicide and the silence of the grave would be a happy release from this nightly agony; perhaps the old instinct comes strong upon me to go after my matches; but my first cool, collected thought is, that the trombone man's destiny is upon him, and he is working it out in suffering and tribulation; and I banish from me the unworthy instinct that would prompt me to burn him out.

After a long immunity from the dreadful insanity that moves a man to become a musician in defiance of the will of God that he should confine himself to sawing wood, I finally fell a victim to the instrument they call the accordion. At this day I hate that contrivance as fervently as any man can, but at the time I speak of I suddenly acquired a disgusting and idolatrous affection for it. I got one of powerful capacity, and learned to play 'Auld Lang Syne' on it. It seems to me, now, that I must have been gifted with a sort of inspiration to be enabled, in the state of ignorance in which I then was, to select out of the whole range of musical composition the one solitary tune that sounds vilest and most distressing on the accordion. I do not suppose there is another tune in the world with which I could have inflicted so much anguish upon my race as I did with that one during my short musical career.

After I had been playing 'Lang Syne' about a week, I had the vanity to think I could improve the original melody, and I set about adding some little flourishes and variations to it, but with rather indifferent success, I suppose, as it brought my landlady into my presence with an expression about her of being opposed to such desperate enterprises. Said she, 'Do you know any other tune but that, Mr Twain?' I told her, meekly, that I did not. 'Well, then,' said she, 'stick to it just as it is; don't put any variations to it, because it's rough enough on the boarders the way it is now.'

The fact is, it was something more than simply 'rough enough' on them; it was altogether too rough; half of them left, and the other half would have followed, but Mrs Jones saved them by discharging me from the premises.

I only stayed one night at my next lodginghouse. Mrs Smith was after me early in the morning. She said, 'You can go, sir; I don't want you here; I have had one of your kind before – a poor lunatic, that played the banjo and danced breakdowns, and jarred the glass all out of the windows. You kept me awake all night, and if you was to do it again, I'd take and mash that thing over your head!' I could see that this woman took no delight in music, and I moved to Mrs Brown's.

For three nights in succession I gave my new neighbors 'Auld Lang Syne', plain and unadulterated, save by a few discords that rather improved the general effect than otherwise. But the very first time I tried the variations the boarders mutinied. I never did find anybody that would stand those variations. I was very well satisfied with my efforts in that house, however, and I left it without any regrets; I drove one boarder as mad as a March hare, and another one tried to scalp his mother. I reflected, though, that if I could only have been allowed to give this latter just one more touch of the variations, he would have finished the old woman.

I went to board at Mrs Murphy's, an Italian lady of many excellent qualities. The very first time I struck up the variations, a haggard, care-worn, cadaverous old man walked into my room and stood beaming upon me a smile of ineffable happiness. Then he placed his hand upon my head, and looking devoutly aloft, he said with feeling unction, and in a voice trembling with emotion, 'God bless you, young man! God bless you! for you have done that for me which is beyond all praise. For years I have suffered from an incurable disease, and knowing my doom was sealed and that I must die, I have striven with all my power to resign myself to my fate, but in vain – the love of life was too strong within me. But Heaven bless you, my benefactor! for since I heard you play that tune and those variations, I do not want to live any longer – I am entirely resigned – I am willing to die – in fact, I am anxious to die.' And then the old man fell upon my neck and wept a flood of happy tears. I was surprised at these things; but I could not help feeling a little proud at what I had done, nor could I help giving the old gentleman a parting blast in the way of some peculiarly lacerating variations as he went out at the door. They doubled him up like a jack-knife, and the next time he left his bed of pain and suffering he was all right, in a metallic coffin.

My passion for the accordion finally spent itself and died out, and I was glad when I found myself free from its unwholesome influence. While the fever was upon me, I was a living, breathing calamity wherever I went, and desolation and disaster followed in my wake. I bred discord in families, I crushed the spirits of the light-hearted, I drove the melancholy to despair, I hurried invalids to premature dissolution, and I fear me I disturbed the very dead in their graves. I did incalculable harm, and inflicted untold suffering upon my race with my execrable music; and yet to atone for it all, I did but one single blessed act, in making that weary old man willing to go to his long home.

Still, I derived some little benefit from that accordion; for while I continued to practice on it, I never had to pay any board – landlords were always willing to compromise, on my leaving before the month was up.

Now, I had two objects in view in writing the foregoing, one of which was to try and reconcile people to those poor unfortunates who feel that they have a genius for music, and who drive their neighbors crazy every night in trying to develop and cultivate it; and the other was to introduce an admirable story about Little George Washington, who could Not Lie, and the Cherry-Tree – or the Apple-Tree – I have forgotten now which, although it was told me only yesterday. And writing such a long and elaborate introductory has caused me to forget the story itself; but it was very touching.

A Complaint
About Correspondents

What do you take us for, on this side of the continent? I am addressing myself personally, and with asperity, to every man, woman, and child east of the Rocky Mountains. How do you suppose our minds are constituted, that you will write us such execrable letters – such poor, bald, uninteresting trash? You complain that by the time a man has been on the Pacific coast six months, he seems to lose all concern about matters and things and people in the distant East, and ceases to answer the letters of his friends and even his relatives. It is your own fault. You need a lecture on the subject – a lecture which ought to read about as follows:

There is only one brief, solitary law for letter-writing, and yet you either do not know that law, or else you are so stupid that you never think of it. It is very easy and simple: Write only about things and people your correspondent takes a living interest in.

Can not you remember that law, hereafter, and abide by it? If you are an old friend of the person you are writing to, you know a number of his acquaintances, and you can rest satisfied that even the most trivial things you can write about them will be read with avidity out here on the edge of sunset.

Yet how *do* you write? – how do the most of you write? Why, you drivel and drivel and drivel along in your wooden-headed way about people one never heard of before, and things which one knows nothing at all about and cares less. There is no sense in that. Let me show up your style with a specimen or so. Here is a paragraph from my Aunt Nancy's last letter – received four years ago, and not answered immediately – not at all, I may say:

St Louis, 1862

DEAR MARK:

We spent the evening very pleasantly at home yesterday. The Rev. Dr Macklin and wife, from Peoria, were here. He is an humble laborer in the vineyard, and takes his coffee strong. He is also subject to neuralgia – neuralgia in the head – and is so unassuming and prayerful. There are few such men. We had soup for dinner likewise. Although I am not fond of it. O Mark! why *don't* you try to lead a better life? Read II Kings, from chap. 2 to chap. 24 inclusive. It would be so gratifying to me if you would experience a change of heart. Poor Mrs Gabrick is dead. You did not know her. She had fits, poor soul. On the 14th the entire army took up the line of march from—

I always stopped there, because I knew what was coming – the war news, in minute and dry detail – for I could never drive it into those numskulls that the overland telegraph enabled me to know here in San Francisco every day all that transpired in the United States the day before, and that the pony express brought me exhaustive details of all matters pertaining to the war at least two weeks before their letters could possibly reach me. So I naturally skipped their stale war reports, even at the cost of also skipping the inevitable suggestions to read this, that, and the other batch of chapters in the Scriptures, with which they were interlarded at intervals, like snares wherewith to trap the unwary sinner.

Now what was the Rev. Macklin to me? Of what consequence was it to me that he was 'an humble laborer in the vineyard', and 'took his coffee strong'? – and was 'unassuming', and 'neuralgic', and 'prayerful'? Such a strange conglomeration of virtues could only excite my admiration – nothing more. It could awake no living interest. That there are few such men, and that we had soup for dinner, is simply gratifying – that is all. 'Read twenty-two chapters of II Kings' is a nice shell to fall in the camp of a man who is not studying for the ministry. The intelligence that 'poor Mrs Gabrick' was dead, aroused no enthusiasm – mostly because of the circumstance that I had never heard of her before, I presume. But I was glad she had fits – although a stranger.

Don't you begin to understand, now? Don't you see that there is not a sentence in that letter of any interest in the world to me? I had the war news in advance of it; I could get a much better sermon at church when I needed it; I didn't care anything about poor Gabrick, not knowing deceased; nor yet the Rev.

Macklin, not knowing him either. I said to myself, 'Here's not a word about Mary Anne Smith – I wish there was; nor about Georgiana Brown, or Zeb Leavenworth, or Sam Bowen, or Strother Wiley – or about anybody else I care a straw for.' And so, as this letter was just of a pattern with all that went before it, it was not answered, and one useless correspondence ceased.

My venerable mother is a tolerably good correspondent – she is above the average, at any rate. She puts on her spectacles and takes her scissors and wades into a pile of newspapers, and slashes out column after column – editorials, hotel arrivals, poetry, telegraph news, advertisements, novelettes, old jokes, recipes for making pies, cures for 'biles' – anything that comes handy; it don't matter to her; she is entirely impartial; she slashes out a column, and runs her eye down it over her spectacles (she looks over them because she can't see through them, but she prefers them to her more serviceable ones because they have got gold rims to them), runs her eye down the column, and says, 'Well, it's from a St Louis paper, anyway,' and jams it into the envelope along with her letter. She writes about everybody I ever knew or ever heard of; but unhappily, she forgets that when she tells me that 'J. B. is dead', and that 'W. L. is going to marry T. D.' and that 'B. K. and R. M. and L. P. J. have all gone to New Orleans to live', it is more than likely that years of absence may have so dulled my recollection of once familiar names, that their unexplained initials will be as unintelligible as Hebrew unto me. She never writes a name in full, and so I never know whom she is talking about. Therefore I have to guess – and this was how it came that I mourned the death of Bill Kribben when I should have rejoiced over the dissolution of Ben Kenfuron. I failed to cipher the initials out correctly.

The most useful and interesting letters we get here from home are from children seven or eight years old. This is petrified truth. Happily they have got nothing to talk about but home, and neighbors, and family – things their betters think unworthy of transmission thousands of miles. They write simply and naturally, and without straining for effect. They tell all they know, and then stop. They seldom deal in abstractions or moral homilies. Consequently their epistles are brief; but, treating as they do of familiar scenes and persons, always entertaining. Now, therefore, if you would learn the art of letter-writing, let a little child teach you. I have preserved a letter from a small girl eight years of age – preserved it as a curiosity, because it was the only letter I ever got from the States that had any information in it. It runs thus:

St Louis, 1865

UNCLE MARK,

If you was here, I could tell you about Moses in the Bulrushers again, I know it better now. Mr Sowerby has got his leg broke off a horse. He was riding it on Sunday. Margaret, that's the maid, Margaret has took all the spittoons, and slop-buckets, and old jugs out of your room, because she says she don't think you're ever coming back any more, you been gone so long. Sissy McElroy's mother has got another little baby. She has them all the time. It has got little blue eyes, like Mr Swimley that boards there, and looks just like him. I have got a new doll, but Johnny Anderson pulled one of its legs out. Miss Doosenberry was here today; I give her your picture, but she said she didn't want it. My cat has got more kittens – oh! you can't think – twice as many as Lottie Belden's. And there's one, such a sweet little buff one with a short tail, and I named it for you. All of them's got names now – General Grant, and Halleck, and Moses, and Margaret, and Deuteronomy, and Captain Semmes, and Exodus, and Leviticus, and Horace Greeley – all named but one, and I am saving it because the one that I named for You's been sick all the time since, and I reckon it'll die. [It appears to have been mighty rough on the short-tailed kitten, naming it for me – I wonder how the reserved victim will stand it.] Uncle Mark, I do believe Hattie Caldwell likes you, and I know she thinks you are pretty, because I heard her say nothing couldn't hurt your good looks – nothing at all – she said, even if you was to have the small-pox ever so bad, you would be just as good-looking as you was before. And my ma says she's ever so smart. [Very.] So no more this time, because General Grant and Moses is fighting.

ANNIE

This child treads on my toes, in every other sentence, with a perfect looseness, but in the simplicity of her time of life she doesn't know it.

I consider that a model letter – an eminently readable and entertaining letter, and, as I said before, it contains more matter of interest and more real information than any letter I ever received from the East. I had rather hear about the cats at home and their truly remarkable names, than listen to a lot of stuff about people I am not acquainted with, or read 'The Evil Effects of the Intoxicating Bowl', illustrated on the back with a picture of a ragged scalliwag pelting away right and left, in the midst of his family circle, with a junk bottle.

The Story of the Bad Little Boy Who Didn't Come to Grief

Once there was a bad little boy, whose name was Jim – though, if you will notice, you will find that bad little boys are nearly always called James in your Sunday-school books. It was very strange, but still it was true, that this one was simply called Jim.

He didn't have any sick mother, either – a sick mother who was pious and had the consumption, and would be glad to lie down in the grave and be at rest, but for the strong love she bore her boy, and the anxiety she felt that the world would be harsh and cold toward him when she was gone. Most bad boys in the Sunday books are named James, and have sick mothers, who teach them to say, 'Now I lay me down', etc., and sing them to sleep with sweet plaintive voices, and then kiss them good night, and kneel down by the bedside and weep. But it was different with this fellow. He was named Jim, and there wasn't anything the matter with his mother – no consumption, or anything of that kind. She was rather stout than otherwise, and she was not pious; moreover, she was not anxious on Jim's account. She said if he were to break his neck, it wouldn't be much loss. She always spanked Jim to sleep, and she never kissed him good night; on the contrary, she boxed his ears when she was ready to leave him.

Once this little bad boy stole the key of the pantry and slipped in there and helped himself to some jam, and filled up the vessel with tar, so that his mother would never know the difference; but all at once a terrible feeling didn't come over him, and something didn't seem to whisper to him, 'Is it right to disobey my mother? Isn't it sinful to do this? Where do bad little boys go who gobble up their good kind mother's jam?' and then he didn't kneel down all alone and promise never to be wicked any more, and rise up with a light, happy heart, and go and tell his mother all about it, and beg her forgiveness, and be blessed by her with tears of pride and thankfulness in her eyes. No; that is the way with all other bad boys in the books; but it happened otherwise with this Jim, strangely enough. He ate that jam, and

said it was bully, in his sinful, vulgar way; and he put in the tar, and said that was bully also, and laughed, and observed 'that the old woman would get up and snort' when she found it out; and when she did find it out, he denied knowing anything about it, and she whipped him severely, and he did the crying himself. Everything about this boy was curious – everything turned out differently with him from the way it does to the bad Jameses in the books.

Once he climbed up Farmer Acorn's apple-tree to steal apples, and the limb didn't break, and he didn't fall and break his arm, and get torn by the farmer's great dog, and then languish on a sick-bed for weeks, and repent and become good. Oh! no; he stole as many apples as he wanted, and came down all right; and he was all ready for the dog too, and knocked him endways with a brick when he came to tear him. It was very strange – nothing like it ever happened in those mild little books with marbled backs, and with pictures in them of men with swallow-tailed coats, and bell-crowned hats, and pantaloons that are short in the legs, and women with the waists of their dresses under their arms, and no hoops on. Nothing like it in any of the Sunday-school books.

Once he stole the teacher's penknife, and when he was afraid it would be found out, and he would get whipped, he slipped it into George Wilson's cap – poor Widow Wilson's son, the moral boy, the good little boy of the village, who always obeyed his mother, and never told an untruth, and was fond of his lessons and infatuated with Sunday-school. And when the knife dropped from the cap, and poor George hung his head and blushed, as if in conscious guilt, and the grieved teacher charged the theft upon him, and was just in the very act of bringing the switch down upon his trembling shoulders, a white-haired improbable justice of the peace did not suddenly appear in their midst and strike an attitude and say 'Spare this noble boy – there stands the cowering culprit! I was passing the school-door at recess, and, unseen myself, I saw the theft committed!' And then Jim didn't get whaled, and the venerable justice didn't read the tearful school a homily, and take George by the hand and say such a boy deserved to be exalted, and then tell him to come and make his home with him, and sweep out the office, and make fires, and run errands, and chop wood, and study law, and help his wife to do household labors, and have all the balance of the time to play, and get forty cents a month, and be happy. No; it would have happened that way in the books, but it didn't happen that way to Jim. No meddling old clam of a justice dropped in to make trouble, and so the model boy George got thrashed, and Jim was glad of it; because, you know, Jim hated moral boys. Jim said he was 'down on them milksops'. Such was the coarse language of this bad, neglected boy.

But the strangest thing that ever happened to Jim was the time he went boating on Sunday and didn't get drowned, and that other time that he got caught out in the storm when he was fishing on Sunday, and didn't get struck by lightning. Why, you might look, and look, and look through the Sunday-school books, from now till next Christmas, and you would never come across anything like this. Oh! no; you would find that all the bad boys who go boating on Sunday invariably get drowned; and all the bad boys who get caught out in storms, when they are fishing on Sunday, infallibly get struck by lightning. Boats with bad boys in them always upset on Sunday, and it always storms when bad boys go fishing on the Sabbath. How this Jim ever escaped is a mystery to me.

This Jim bore a charmed life – that must have been the way of it. Nothing could hurt him. He even gave the elephant in the menagerie a plug of tobacco, and the elephant didn't knock the top of his head off with his trunk. He browsed around the cupboard after essence of peppermint, and didn't make a mistake and drink aquafortis. He stole his father's gun and went hunting on the Sabbath, and didn't shoot three or four of his fingers off. He struck his little sister on the temple with his fist when he was angry, and she didn't linger in pain through long summer days, and die with sweet words of forgiveness upon her lips that redoubled the anguish of his breaking heart. No; she hit back; and she never got sick at all. He ran off and went to sea at last, and didn't come back and find himself sad and alone in the world, his loved ones sleeping in the quiet churchyard, and the vine-embowered home of his boyhood tumbled down and gone to decay. Ah! no; he came home drunk as a piper, and got into the station-house the first thing.

And he grew up, and married, and raised a large family, and brained them all with an axe one night, and got wealthy by all manner of cheating and rascality; and now he is the infernalest wickedest scoundrel in his native village, and is universally respected, and belongs to the Legislature.

So you see there never was a bad James in the Sunday-school books that had such a streak of luck as this sinful Jim with the charmed life.

The Story of the Good Little Boy Who Did Not Prosper

Once there was a good little boy by the name of Jacob Blivens. He always obeyed his parents, no matter how absurd and unreasonable their demands were; and he always learned his book, and never was late at Sabbath school. He would not play hooky, even when his sober judgment told him it was the most profitable thing he could do. None of the other boys could ever make that boy out, he acted so strangely. He wouldn't lie, no matter how convenient it was. He just said it was wrong to lie, and that was sufficient for him. And he was so honest that he was simply ridiculous. The curious ways that that Jacob had surpassed everything. He wouldn't play marbles on Sunday, he wouldn't rob birds' nests, he wouldn't give hot pennies to organ-grinders' monkeys; he didn't seem to take any interest in any kind of rational amusement. So the other boys used to try to reason it out and come to an understanding of him, but they couldn't arrive at any satisfactory conclusion. As I said before, they could only figure out a sort of vague idea that he was 'afflicted', and so they took him under their protection, and never allowed any harm to come to him.

This good little boy read all the Sunday-school books; they were his greatest delight. This was the whole secret of it. He believed in the good little boys they put in the Sunday-school books; he had every confidence in them. He longed to come across one of them alive, once; but he never did. They all died before his time, maybe. Whenever he read about a particularly good one he turned over quickly to the end to see what became of him, because he wanted to travel thousands of miles and gaze on him; but it wasn't any use; that good little boy always died in the last chapter, and there was a picture of the funeral, with all his relations and the Sunday-school children standing around the grave in pantaloons that were too short, and bonnets that were too large, and everybody crying into handkerchiefs that had as much as a yard and a half of stuff in them. He was always

headed off in this way. He never could see one of those good little boys on account of his always dying in the last chapter.

Jacob had a noble ambition to be put in a Sunday-school book. He wanted to be put in, with pictures representing him gloriously declining to lie to his mother, and her weeping for joy about it; and pictures representing him standing on the doorstep giving a penny to a poor beggar-woman with six children, and telling her to spend it freely, but not to be extravagant, because extravagance is a sin; and pictures of him magnanimously refusing to tell on the bad boy who always lay in wait for him around the corner as he came from school, and welted him over the head with a lath, and then chased him home, saying, 'Hi! hi!' as he proceeded. That was the ambition of young Jacob Blivens. He wished to be put in a Sunday-school book. It made him feel a little uncomfortable sometimes when he reflected that the good little boys always died. He loved to live, you know, and this was the most unpleasant feature about being a Sunday-school-book boy. He knew it was not healthy to be good. He knew it was more fatal than consumption to be so supernaturally good as the boys in the books were; he knew that none of them had ever been able to stand it long, and it pained him to think that if they put him in a book he wouldn't ever see it, or even if they did get the book out before he died it wouldn't be popular without any picture of his funeral in the back part of it. It couldn't be much of a Sunday-school book that couldn't tell about the advice he gave to the community when he was dying. So at last, of course, he had to make up his mind to do the best he could under the circumstances – to live right, and hang on as long as he could, and have his dying speech all ready when his time came.

But somehow nothing ever went right with this good little boy; nothing ever turned out with him the way it turned out with the good little boys in the books. They always had a good time, and the bad boys had the broken legs; but in his case there was a screw loose somewhere, and it all happened just the other way. When he found Jim Blake stealing apples, and went under the tree to read to him about the bad little boy who fell out of a neighbour's apple-tree and broke his arm, Jim fell out of the tree too, but he fell on *him*, and broke *his* arm, and Jim wasn't hurt at all. Jacob couldn't understand that. There wasn't anything in the books like it.

And once, when some bad boys pushed a blind man over in the mud, and Jacob ran to help him up and receive his blessing, the blind man did not give him any blessing at all, but whacked him over the head with his stick and said he would like to catch him shoving *him* again, and then pretending to help him up. This was not in accordance with any of the books. Jacob looked them all over to see.

One thing that Jacob wanted to do was to find a lame dog that hadn't any place to stay, and was hungry and persecuted, and bring him home and pet him, and have that dog's imperishable gratitude. And at last he found one and was happy; and he brought him home and fed him, but when he was going to pet him the dog flew at him and tore all the clothes off him except those that were in front, and made a spectacle of him that was astonishing. He examined authorities, but he could not understand the matter. It was of the same breed of dogs that was in the books, but it acted very differently. Whatever this boy did he got into trouble. The very things the boys in the books got rewarded for turned out to be about the most unprofitable things he could invest in.

Once when he was on his way to Sunday-school he saw some bad boys starting off pleasuring in a sail-boat. He was filled with consternation, because he knew from his reading that boys who went sailing on Sunday invariably got drowned. So he ran out on a raft to warn them, but a log turned with him and slid him into the river. A man got him out pretty soon, and the doctor pumped the water out of him, and gave him a fresh start with his bellows, but he caught cold and lay sick a-bed nine weeks. But the most unaccountable thing about it was that the bad boys in the boat had a good time all day, and then reached home alive and well in the most surprising manner. Jacob Blivens said there was nothing like these things in the books. He was perfectly dumb-founded.

When he got well he was a little discouraged, but he resolved to keep on trying anyhow. He knew that so far his experiences wouldn't do to go in a book, but he hadn't yet reached the allotted term of life for good little boys, and he hoped to be able to

74

make a record yet if he could hold on till his time was fully up. If everything else failed he had his dying speech to fall back on.

He examined his authorities, and found that it was now time for him to go to sea as a cabin-boy. He called on a ship captain and made his application, and when the captain asked for his recommendations he proudly drew out a tract and pointed to the words, 'To Jacob Blivens, from his affectionate teacher.' But the captain was a coarse vulgar man, and he said, 'Oh, that be blowed! *that* wasn't any proof that he knew how to wash dishes or handle a slush-bucket, and he guessed he didn't want him.' This was altogether the most extraordinary thing that ever happened to Jacob in all his life. A compliment from a teacher, on a tract, had never failed to move the tenderest emotions of ship captains, and open the way to all offices of honour and profit in their gift – it never had in any book that ever *he* had read. He could hardly believe his senses.

This boy always had a hard time of it. Nothing ever came out according to the authorities with him. At last, one day, when he was around hunting up bad little boys to admonish, he found a lot of them in the old iron foundry fixing up a little joke on fourteen or fifteen dogs, which they had tied together in long procession and were going to ornament with empty nitro-glycerine cans made fast to their tails. Jacob's heart was touched. He sat down on one of those cans (for he never minded grease when duty was before him), and he took hold of the foremost dog by the collar, and turned his reproving eye upon wicked Tom Jones. But just at that moment Alderman McWelter, full of wrath, stepped in. All the bad boys ran away, but Jacob Blivens rose in conscious innocence and began one of those stately little Sunday-school-book speeches which always commence with 'Oh, sir!' in dead opposition to the fact that no boy, good or bad, ever starts a remark with 'Oh, sir!' But the alderman never waited to hear the rest. He took Jacob Blivens by the ear and turned him round, and hit him a whack in the rear with the flat of his hand; and in an instant that good little boy shot out through the roof and soared away toward the sun, with the fragments of those fifteen dogs stringing after him like the tail of a kite. And there wasn't a sign of that alderman or that old iron foundry left on the face of the earth; and, as for young Jacob

Blivens, he never got a chance to make his last dying speech after all his trouble fixing it up, unless he made it to the birds; because, although the bulk of him came down all right in a tree-top in an adjoining county, the rest of him was apportioned around among four townships, and so they had to hold five inquests on him to find out whether he was dead or not, and how it occurred. You never saw a boy scattered so.

Thus perished the good little boy who did the best he could, but didn't come out according to the books. Every boy who ever did as he did prospered except him. His case is truly remarkable. It will probably never be accounted for.*

* This glycerine suggestion is borrowed from a floating newspaper item whose author's name I would give if I knew it. M. T.

The Man That Corrupted Hadleyburg

It was many years ago. Hadleyburg was the most honest and upright town in all the region around about. It had kept that reputation unsmirched during three generations, and was prouder
of it than of any other of its possessions. It was so proud of it, and
so anxious to insure its perpetuation, that it began to teach the
principles of honest dealing to its babies in the cradle, and made
the like teachings the staple of their culture thenceforward
through all the years devoted to their education. Also, throughout the formative years temptations were kept out of the way of
the young people, so that their honesty could have every chance
to harden and solidify, and become a part of their very bone. The
neighboring towns were jealous of this honorable supremacy,
and affected to sneer at Hadleyburg's pride in it and call it vanity;
but all the same they were obliged to acknowledge that Hadleyburg was in reality an incorruptible town; and if pressed they
would also acknowledge that the mere fact that a young man
hailed from Hadleyburg was all the recommendation he needed
when he went forth from his natal town to seek for responsible
employment.

But at last, in the drift of time, Hadleyburg had the ill luck to
offend a passing stranger – possibly without knowing it, certainly without caring, for Hadleyburg was sufficient unto itself,
and cared not a rap for strangers or their opinions. Still, it would
have been well to make an exception in this one's case, for he
was a bitter man and revengeful. All through his wanderings
during a whole year he kept his injury in mind, and gave all his
leisure moments to trying to invent a compensating satisfaction
for it. He contrived many plans, and all of them were good, but
none of them was quite sweeping enough; the poorest of them
would hurt a great many individuals, but what he wanted was a
plan which would comprehend the entire town, and not let so
much as one person escape unhurt. At last he had a fortunate

idea, and when it fell into his brain it lit up his whole head with an evil joy. He began to form a plan at once, saying to himself, 'That is the thing to do – I will corrupt the town.'

Six months later he went to Hadleyburg, and arrived in a buggy at the house of the old cashier of the bank about ten at night. He got a sack out of the buggy, shouldered it, and staggered with it through the cottage yard, and knocked at the door. A woman's voice said, 'Come in,' and he entered, and set his sack behind the stove in the parlor, saying politely to the old lady who sat reading the *Missionary Herald* by the lamp:

'Pray keep your seat, madam, I will not disturb you. There – now it is pretty well concealed; one would hardly know it was there. Can I see your husband a moment, madam?'

No, he was gone to Brixton, and might not return before morning.

'Very well, madam, it is no matter. I merely wanted to leave that sack in his care, to be delivered to the rightful owner when he shall be found. I am a stranger; he does not know me; I am merely passing through the town tonight to discharge a matter which has been long in my mind. My errand is now completed, and I go pleased and a little proud, and you will never see me again. There is a paper attached to the sack which will explain everything. Good night, madam.'

The old lady was afraid of the mysterious big stranger, and was glad to see him go. But her curiosity was roused, and she went straight to the sack and brought away the paper. It began as follows:

TO BE PUBLISHED; or, the right man sought out by private inquiry – either will answer. This sack contains gold coin weighing a hundred and sixty pounds four ounces—

'Mercy on us, and the door not locked!'

Mrs Richards flew to it all in a tremble and locked it, then pulled down the window-shades and stood frightened, worried, and wondering if there was anything else she could do toward making herself and the money more safe. She listened awhile for burglars, then surrendered to curiosity and went back to the lamp and finished reading the paper:

78

I am a foreigner, and am presently going back to my own country, to remain there permanently. I am grateful to America for what I have received at her hands during my long stay under her flag; and to one of her citizens – a citizen of Hadleyburg – I am especially grateful for a great kindness done me a year or two ago. Two great kindnesses, in fact. I will explain. I was a gambler. I say I WAS. I was a ruined gambler. I arrived in this village at night, hungry and without a penny. I asked for help – in the dark; I was ashamed to beg in the light. I begged of the right man. He gave me twenty dollars – that is to say, he gave me life, as I considered it. He also gave me fortune; for out of that money I have made myself rich at the gaming-table. And finally, a remark which he made to me has remained with me to this day, and has at last conquered me; and in conquering has saved the remnant of my morals; I shall gamble no more. Now I have no idea who that man was, but I want him found, and I want him to have this money, to give away, throw away, or keep, as he pleases. It is merely my way of testifying my gratitude to him. If I could stay, I would find him myself; but no matter, he will be found. This is an honest town, an incorruptible town, and I know I can trust it without fear. This man can be identified by the remark which he made to me; I feel persuaded that he will remember it.

And now my plan is this: If you prefer to conduct the inquiry privately, do so. Tell the contents of this present writing to anyone who is likely to be the right man. If he shall answer, 'I am the man; the remark I made was so-and-so,' apply the test – to wit: open the sack, and in it you will find a sealed envelope containing that remark. If the remark mentioned by the candidate tallies with it, give him the money, and ask no further questions, for he is certainly the right man.

But if you shall prefer a public inquiry, then publish this present writing in the local paper – with these instructions added, to wit: Thirty days from now, let the candidate appear at the town-hall at eight in the evening (Friday), and hand his remark, in a sealed envelope, to the Rev. Mr Burgess (if he will be kind enough to act); and let Mr Burgess there and then destroy the seals of the sack, open it, and see if the remark is correct; if correct, let the money be delivered, with my sincere gratitude, to my benefactor thus identified.

Mrs Richards sat down, gently quivering with excitement, and was soon lost in thinkings – after this pattern: 'What a strange thing it is! . . . And what a fortune for that kind man who set his bread afloat upon the waters! . . . If it had only been my husband that did it! – for we are so poor, so old and poor! . . .' Then, with a sigh – 'But it was not my Edward; no, it was not he that gave a stranger twenty dollars. It is a pity, too; I see it now . . .' Then, with a shudder – 'But it is *gambler's* money! the wages of sin: we couldn't take it; we couldn't touch it. I don't like to be near it; it seems a defilement.' She moved to a further chair . . . 'I wish Edward would come and take it to the bank; a burglar might come at any moment; it is dreadful to be here all alone with it.'

At eleven Mr Richards arrived, and while his wife was saying, 'I am *so* glad you've come!' he was saying, 'I'm so tired – tired clear out; it is dreadful to be poor, and have to make these dismal journeys at my time of life. Always at the grind, grind, grind, on a salary – another man's slave, and he sitting at home in his slippers, rich and comfortable.'

'I am so sorry for you, Edward, you know that; but be comforted: we have our livelihood; we have our good name—'

'Yes, Mary, and that is everything. Don't mind my talk – it's just a moment's irritation and doesn't mean anything. Kiss me – there, it's all gone now, and I am not complaining any more. What have you been getting? What's in the sack?'

Then his wife told him the great secret. It dazed him for a moment; then he said:

'It weighs a hundred and sixty pounds? Why, Mary, it's forty thousand dollars – think of it – a whole fortune! Not ten men in this village are worth that much. Give me the paper.'

He skimmed through it and said:

'Isn't it an adventure! Why, it's a romance; it's like the impossible things one reads about in books, and never sees in life.' He was well stirred up now; cheerful, even gleeful. He tapped his old wife on the cheek, and said, humorously, 'Why, we're rich, Mary, rich; all we've got to do is to bury the money and burn the papers. If the gambler ever comes to inquire, we'll merely look coldly upon him and say: "What is this nonsense you are talking? We have never heard of you and your sack of gold before"; and then he would look foolish, and—'

'And in the mean time, while you are running on with your jokes, the money is still here, and it is fast getting along toward burglar-time.'

'True. Very well, what shall we do – make the inquiry private? No, not that: it would spoil the romance. The public method is better. Think what a noise it will make! And it will make all the other towns jealous; for no stranger would trust such a thing to any town but Hadleyburg, and they know it. It's a great card for us. I must get to the printing-office now, or I shall be too late.'

'But stop – stop – don't leave me here alone with it, Edward!'

But he was gone. For only a little while, however. Not far from his own house he met the editor-proprietor of the paper, and gave him the document, and said, 'Here is a good thing for you, Cox – put it in.'

'It may be too late, Mr Richards, but I'll see.'

At home again he and his wife sat down to talk the charming mystery over; they were in no condition for sleep. The first question was, Who could the citizen have been who gave the stranger the twenty dollars? It seemed a simple one; both answered it in the same breath:

'Barclay Goodson.'

'Yes,' said Richards, 'he could have done it, and it would have been like him, but there's not another in the town.'

'Everybody will grant that, Edward – grant it privately, any-way. For six months, now, the village has been its own proper self once more – honest, narrow, self-righteous, and stingy.'

'It is what he always called it, to the day of his death – said it right out publicly, too.'

'Yes, and he was hated for it.'

'Oh, of course; but he didn't care. I reckon he was the best-hated man among us, except the Reverend Burgess.'

'Well, Burgess deserves it – he will never get another congre-gation here. Mean as the town is, it knows how to estimate *him*. Edward, doesn't it seem odd that the stranger should appoint Burgess to deliver the money?'

'Well, yes – it does. That is – that is—'

'Why so much that-*is*-ing? Would *you* select him?'

'Mary, maybe the stranger knows him better than this village does.'

'Much *that* would help Burgess!'

The husband seemed perplexed for an answer; the wife kept a steady eye upon him, and waited. Finally Richards said, with the hesitancy of one who is making a statement which is likely to encounter doubt:

'Mary, Burgess is not a bad man.'

His wife was certainly surprised.

'Nonsense!' she exclaimed.

'He is not a bad man. I know. The whole of his unpopularity had its foundation in that one thing – the thing that made so much noise.'

'That "one thing", indeed! As if that "one thing" wasn't enough, all by itself.'

'Plenty. Plenty. Only he wasn't guilty of it.'

'How you talk! Not guilty of it! Everybody knows he *was* guilty.'

'Mary, I give you my word – he was innocent.'

'I can't believe it, and I don't. How do you know?'

'It is a confession. I am ashamed, but I will make it. I was the only man who knew he was innocent. I could have saved him, and – and – well, you know how the town was wrought up – I hadn't the pluck to do it. It would have turned everybody against me. I felt mean, ever so mean; but I didn't dare; I hadn't the manliness to face that.'

Mary looked troubled, and for a while was silent. Then she said, stammeringly:

'I – I don't think it would have done for you to – to— One mustn't – er – public opinion – one has to be so careful – so—' It was a difficult road, and she got mired; but after a little she got started again. 'It was a great pity, but— Why, we couldn't afford it, Edward – we couldn't indeed. Oh, I wouldn't have had you do it for anything!'

'It would have lost us the good will of so many people, Mary; and then – and then—'

'What troubles me now is, what *he* thinks of us, Edward.'

'He? *He* doesn't suspect that I could have saved him.'

'Oh,' exclaimed the wife, in a tone of relief, 'I am glad of that! As long as he doesn't know that you could have saved him, he – he – well, that makes it a great deal better. Why, I might have

82

known he didn't know, because he is always trying to be friendly with us, as little encouragement as we give him. More than once people have twitted me with it. There's the Wilsons, and the Wilcoxes, and the Harknesses, they take a mean pleasure in saying, "*Your friend* Burgess," because they know it pesters me. I wish he wouldn't persist in liking us so; I can't think why he keeps it up.'

'I can explain it. It's another confession. When the thing was new and hot, and the town made a plan to ride him on a rail, my conscience hurt me so that I couldn't stand it, and I went privately and gave him notice, and he got out of the town and stayed out till it was safe to come back.'

'Edward! If the town had found it out—'

'*Don't!* It scares me yet, to think of it. I repented of it the minute it was done; and I was even afraid to tell you, lest your face might betray it to somebody. I didn't sleep any that night, for worrying. But after a few days I saw that no one was going to suspect me, and after that I got to feeling glad I did it. And I feel glad yet, Mary – glad through and through.'

'So do I, now, for it would have been a dreadful way to treat him. Yes, I'm glad; for really you did owe him that, you know. But, Edward, suppose it should come out yet, some day!'

'It won't.'

'Why?'

'Because everybody thinks it was Goodson.'

'Of course they would!'

'Certainly. And of course *he* didn't care. They persuaded poor old Sawlsberry to go and charge it on him, and he went blustering over there and did it. Goodson looked him over, like as if he was hunting for a place on him that he could despise the most, then he says, "So you are the Committee of Inquiry, are you?" Sawlsberry said that was about what he was. "Hm. Do they require particulars, or do you reckon a kind of a *general* answer will do?" "If they require particulars, I will come back, Mr Goodson; I will take the general answer first." "Very well, then, tell them to go to hell – I reckon that's general enough. And I'll give you some advice, Sawlsberry; when you come back for the particulars, fetch a basket to carry the relics of yourself home in." '

'Just like Goodson; it's got all the marks. He had only one vanity: he thought he could give advice better than any other person.'

'It settled the business, and saved us, Mary. The subject was dropped.'

'Bless you, I'm not doubting *that*.'

Then they took up the gold-sack mystery again, with strong interest. Soon the conversation began to suffer breaks – interruptions caused by absorbed thinkings. The breaks grew more and more frequent. At last Richards lost himself wholly in thought. He sat long, gazing vacantly at the floor, and by and by he began to punctuate his thoughts with little nervous movements of his hands that seemed to indicate vexation. Meantime his wife too had relapsed into a thoughtful silence, and her movements were beginning to show a troubled discomfort. Finally Richards got up and strode aimlessly about the room, plowing his hands through his hair, much as a somnambulist might do who was having a bad dream. Then he seemed to arrive at a definite purpose; and without a word he put on his hat and passed quickly out of the house. His wife sat brooding, with a drawn face, and did not seem to be aware that she was alone. Now and then she murmured, 'Lead us not into t— . . . but – but – we are so poor, so poor! . . . Lead us not into . . . Ah, who would be hurt by it? – and no one would ever know . . . Lead us . . .' The voice died out in mumblings. After a little she glanced up and muttered in a half-frightened, half-glad way:

'He is gone! But, oh dear, he may be too late – too late . . . Maybe not – maybe there is still time.' She rose and stood thinking, nervously clasping and unclasping her hands. A slight shudder shook her frame, and she said, out of a dry throat, 'God forgive me – it's awful to think such things – but . . . Lord, how we are made – how strangely we are made!'

She turned the light low, and slipped stealthily over and kneeled down by the sack and felt of its ridgy sides with her hands, and fondled them lovingly; and there was a gloating light in her poor old eyes. She fell into fits of absence; and came half out of them at times to mutter, 'If we had only waited! – oh, if we had only waited a little, and not been in such a hurry!'

Meantime Cox had gone home from his office and told his

wife all about the strange thing that had happened, and they had talked it over eagerly, and guessed that the late Goodson was the only man in the town who could have helped a suffering stranger with so noble a sum as twenty dollars. Then there was a pause, and the two became thoughtful and silent. And by and by nervous and fidgety. At last the wife said, as if to herself:

'Nobody knows this secret but the Richardses . . . and us . . . nobody.'

The husband came out of his thinkings with a slight start, and gazed wistfully at his wife, whose face was become very pale; then he hesitatingly rose, and glanced furtively at his hat, then at his wife – a sort of mute inquiry. Mrs Cox swallowed once or twice, with her hand at her throat, then in place of speech she nodded her head. In a moment she was alone, and mumbling to herself.

And now Richards and Cox were hurrying through the deserted streets, from opposite directions. They met, panting, at the foot of the printing-office stairs; by the night light there they read each other's face. Cox whispered:

'Nobody knows about this but us?'

The whispered answer was,

'Not a soul – on honor, not a soul!'

'If it isn't too late to—'

The men were starting upstairs; at this moment they were overtaken by a boy, and Cox asked:

'Is that you, Johnny?'

'Yes, sir.'

'You needn't ship the early mail – nor *any* mail; wait till I tell you.'

'It's already gone, sir.'

'*Gone?*' It had the sound of an unspeakable disappointment in it.

'Yes, sir. Time-table for Brixton and all the towns beyond changed today, sir – had to get the papers in twenty minutes earlier than common. I had to rush; if I had been two minutes later—'

The men turned and walked slowly away, not waiting to hear the rest. Neither of them spoke during ten minutes; then Cox said, in a vexed tone:

'What possessed you to be in such a hurry, I can't make out.'

The answer was humble enough:

'I see it now, but somehow I never thought, you know, until it was too late. But the next time—'

'Next time be hanged! It won't come in a thousand years.'

Then the friends separated without a good night, and dragged themselves home with the gait of mortally stricken men. At their homes their wives sprang up with an eager 'Well?' – then saw the answer with their eyes and sank down sorrowing, without waiting for it to come in words. In both houses a discussion followed of a heated sort – a new thing; there had been discussions before, but not heated ones, not ungentle ones. The discussions tonight were a sort of seeming plagiarisms of each other. Mrs Richards said,

'If you had only waited, Edward – if you had only stopped to think; but no, you must run straight to the printing-office and spread it all over the world.'

'It *said* publish it.'

'That is nothing; it also said do it privately, if you liked. There, now – is that true, or not?'

'Why, yes – yes, it is true; but when I thought what a stir it would make, and what a compliment it was to Hadleyburg that a stranger should trust it so—'

'Oh, certainly, I know all that; but if you had only stopped to think, you would have seen that you *couldn't* find the right man, because he is in his grave, and hasn't left chick nor child nor relation behind him; and as long as the money went to somebody that awfully needed it, and nobody would be hurt by it, and – and—'

She broke down, crying. Her husband tried to think of some comforting thing to say, and presently came out with this:

'But after all, Mary, it must be for the best – it *must* be; we know that. And we must remember that it was so ordered—'

'Ordered! Oh, everything's *ordered*, when a person has to find some way out when he has been stupid. Just the same, it was *ordered* that the money should come to us in this special way, and it was you that must take it on yourself to go meddling with the designs of Providence – and who gave you the right? It was wicked, that is what it was – just blasphemous presumption, and no more becoming to a meek and humble professor of—'

'But, Mary, you know how we have been trained all our lives long, like the whole village, till it is absolutely second nature to us to stop not a single moment to think when there's an honest thing to be done—'

'Oh, I know it, I know it – it's been one everlasting training and training and training in honesty – honesty shielded, from the very cradle, against every possible temptation, and so it's *artificial* honesty, and weak as water when temptation comes, as we have seen this night. God knows I never had shade nor shadow of a doubt of my petrified and indestructible honesty until now – and now, under the very first big and real tempta-tion, I – Edward, it is my belief that this town's honesty is as rotten as mine is; as rotten as yours is. It is a mean town, a hard, stingy town, and hasn't a virtue in the world but this honesty it is so celebrated for and so conceited about; and so help me, I do believe that if ever the day comes that its honesty falls under great temptation, its grand reputation will go to ruin like a house of cards. There, now, I've made confession, and I feel better; I am a humbug, and I've been one all my life, without knowing it. Let no man call me honest again – I will not have it.'

'I – well, Mary, I feel a good deal as you do; I certainly do. It seems strange, too, so strange. I never could have believed it – never.'

A long silence followed; both were sunk in thought. At last the wife looked up and said:

'I know what you are thinking, Edward.'

Richards had the embarrassed look of a person who is caught.

'I am ashamed to confess it, Mary, but—'

'It's no matter, Edward, I was thinking the same question myself.'

'I hope so. State it.'

'You were thinking, if a body could only guess out *what the remark was* that Goodson made to the stranger.'

'It's perfectly true. I feel guilty and ashamed. And you?'

'I'm past it. Let us make a pallet here; we've got to stand watch till the bank vault opens in the morning and admits the sack . . . Oh dear, oh dear – if we hadn't made the mistake!'

The pallet was made, and Mary said:

'The open sesame – what could it have been? I do wonder what that remark could have been? But come; we will get to bed now.'

'And sleep?'

'No: think.'

'Yes, think.'

By this time the Coxes too had completed their spat and their reconciliation, and were turning in – to think, to think, and toss, and fret, and worry over what the remark could possibly have been which Goodson made to the stranded derelict; that golden remark; that remark worth forty thousand dollars, cash.

The reason that the village telegraph-office was open later than usual that night was this: The foreman of Cox's paper was the local representative of the Associated Press. One might say its honorary representative, for it wasn't four times a year that he could furnish thirty words that would be accepted. But this time it was different. His despatch stating what he had caught got an instant answer:

SEND THE WHOLE THING – ALL THE DETAILS –TWELVE HUNDRED WORDS.

A colossal order! The foreman filled the bill; and he was the proudest man in the State. By breakfast-time the next morning the name of Hadleyburg the Incorruptible was on every lip in America, from Montreal to the Gulf, from the glaciers of Alaska to the orange-groves of Florida; and millions and millions of people were discussing the stranger and his money-sack, and wondering if the right man would be found, and hoping some more news about the matter would come soon – right away.

2

Hadleyburg village woke up world-celebrated – astonished – happy – vain. Vain beyond imagination. Its nineteen principal citizens and their wives went about shaking hands with each other, and beaming, and smiling, and congratulating, and saying *this* thing adds a new word to the dictionary – *Hadleyburg*, synonym for *incorruptible* – destined to live in dictionaries for ever!

And the minor and unimportant citizens and their wives went around acting in much the same way. Everybody ran to the bank to see the gold-sack; and before noon grieved and envious crowds began to flock in from Brixton and all neighboring towns; and that afternoon and next day reporters began to arrive from everywhere to verify the sack and its history and write the whole thing up anew, and make dashing free-hand pictures of the sack, and of Richards's house, and the bank, and the Presbyterian church, and the Baptist church, and the public square, and the town-hall where the test would be applied and the money delivered; and damnable portraits of the Richardses, and Pinkerton the banker, and Cox, and the foreman, and Reverend Burgess, and the postmaster – and even of Jack Halliday, who was the loafing, good-natured, no-account, irreverent fisherman, hunter, boys' friend, stray-dogs' friend, typical 'Sam Lawson' of the town. The little mean, smirking, oily Pinkerton showed the sack to all comers, and rubbed his sleek palms together pleasantly, and enlarged upon the town's fine old reputation for honesty and upon this wonderful endorsement of it, and hoped and believed that the example would now spread far and wide over the American world, and be epoch-making in the matter of moral regeneration. And so on, and so on.

By the end of a week things had quieted down again; the wild intoxication of pride and joy had sobered to a soft, sweet, silent delight – a sort of deep, nameless, unutterable content. All faces bore a look of peaceful, holy happiness.

Then a change came. It was a gradual change: so gradual that its beginnings were hardly noticed; maybe were not noticed at all, except by Jack Halliday, who always noticed everything; and always made fun of it, too, no matter what it was. He began to throw out chaffing remarks about people not looking quite so happy as they did a day or two ago; and next he claimed that the new aspect was deepening to positive sadness; next, that it was taking on a sick look; and finally he said that everybody was become so moody, thoughtful, and absent-minded that he could rob the meanest man in town of a cent out of the bottom of his breeches pocket and not disturb his revery.

At this stage – or at about this stage – a saying like this was dropped at bedtime – with a sigh, usually – by the head of each of the nineteen principal households: 'Ah, what *could* have been the remark that Goodson made?'

And straightway – with a shudder – came this, from the man's wife:

'Oh, *don't!* What horrible thing are you mulling in your mind? Put it away from you, for God's sake!'

But that question was wrung from those men again the next night – and got the same retort. But weaker.

And the third night the men uttered the question yet again – with anguish, and absently. This time – and the following night – the wives fidgeted feebly, and tried to say something. But didn't.

And the night after that they found their tongues and responded – longingly:

'Oh, if we *could* only guess!'

Halliday's comments grew daily more and more sparklingly disagreeable and disparaging. He went diligently about, laughing at the town, individually and in mass. But his laugh was the only one left in the village: it fell upon a hollow and mournful vacancy and emptiness. Not even a smile was findable anywhere. Halliday carried a cigar-box around on a tripod, playing that it was a camera, and halted all passers and aimed the thing and said, 'Ready! – now look pleasant, please,' but not even this capital joke could surprise the dreary faces into any softening.

So three weeks passed – one week was left. It was Saturday evening – after supper. Instead of the aforetime Saturday-evening flutter and bustle and shopping and larking, the streets were empty and desolate. Richards and his old wife sat apart in their little parlor – miserable and thinking. This was become their evening habit now: the lifelong habit which had preceded it, of reading, knitting, and contented chat, or receiving or paying neighborly calls, was dead and gone and forgotten, ages ago – two or three weeks ago; nobody talked now, nobody read, nobody visited – the whole village sat at home, sighing, worrying, silent. Trying to guess out that remark.

The postman left a letter. Richards glanced listlessly at the superscription and the postmark – unfamiliar, both – and tossed the letter on the table and resumed his might-have-beens and his hopeless dull miseries where he had left them off. Two or three hours later his wife got wearily up and was going away to bed without a good night – custom now – but she stopped near the letter and eyed it awhile with a dead interest, then broke it open, and began to skim it over. Richards, sitting there with his chair tilted back against the wall and his chin between his knees, heard something fall. It was his wife. He sprang to her side, but she cried out:

'Leave me alone, I am too happy. Read the letter – read it!'

He did. He devoured it, his brain reeling. The letter was from a distant state, and it said:

I am a stranger to you, but no matter: I have something to tell. I have just arrived home from Mexico, and learned about that episode. Of course you do not know who made that remark, but I know, and I am the only person living who does know. It was GOODSON. I knew him well, many years ago. I passed through your village that very night, and was his guest till the midnight train came along. I overheard him make that remark to the stranger in the dark – it was in Hale Alley. He and I talked of it the rest of the way home, and while smoking in his house. He mentioned many of your villagers in the course of his talk – most of them in a very uncomplimentary way, but two or three favorably; among these latter yourself. I say 'favorably' – nothing stronger. I remember his saying he did not actually LIKE any person in the town – not one; but that you – I THINK he said you – am almost sure – had done him a very great service once, possibly without knowing the full value of it, and he wished he had a fortune, he would leave it to you when he died, and a curse apiece for the rest of the citizens. Now, then, if it was you that did him that service, you are his legitimate heir, and entitled to the sack of gold. I know that I can trust to your honor and honesty, for in a citizen of Hadleyburg these virtues are an unfailing inheritance, and so I am going to reveal to you the remark, well satisfied that if you are not the right man you will seek and find the right one and see that poor Goodson's debt of gratitude for the service referred to is paid. This is the remark: 'YOU ARE FAR FROM BEING A BAD MAN: GO, AND REFORM.'

HOWARD L. STEPHENSON

'Oh, Edward, the money is ours, and I am so grateful, *oh*, so grateful – kiss me, dear, it's forever since we kissed – and we needed it so – the money – and now you are free of Pinkerton and his bank, and nobody's slave any more; it seems to me I could fly for joy.'

It was a happy half-hour that the couple spent there on the settee caressing each other; it was the old days come again – days that had begun with their courtship and lasted without a break till the stranger brought the deadly money. By and by the wife said:

'Oh, Edward, how lucky it was you did him that grand service, poor Goodson! I never liked him, but I love him now. And it was fine and beautiful of you never to mention it or brag about it.' Then, with a touch of reproach, 'But you ought to have told *me*, Edward, you ought to have told your wife, you know.'

'Well, I – er – well, Mary, you see—'

'Now stop hemming and hawing, and tell me about it, Edward. I always loved you, and now I'm proud of you. Everybody believes there was only one good generous soul in this village, and now it turns out that you— Edward, why don't you tell me?'

'Well – er – er—Why, Mary, I can't!'

'You *can't*? *Why* can't you?'

'You see, he – well, he – he made me promise I wouldn't.'

The wife looked him over, and said, very slowly:

'Made – you – promise? Edward, what do you tell me that for?'

'Mary, do you think I would lie?'

She was troubled and silent for a moment, then she laid her hand within his and said:

'No . . . no. We have wandered far enough from our bearings – God spare us that! In all your life you have never uttered a lie. But now – now that the foundations of things seem to be crumbling from under us, we – we—' She lost her voice for a moment, then said, brokenly, 'Lead us not into temptation . . . I think you made the promise, Edward. Let it rest so. Let us keep away from that ground. Now – that is all gone by; let us be happy again; it is no time for clouds.'

Edward found it something of an effort to comply, for his mind kept wandering – trying to remember what the service was that he had done Goodson.

The couple lay awake the most of the night, Mary happy and busy, Edward busy but not so happy. Mary was planning what she would do with the money. Edward was trying to recall that service. At first his conscience was sore on account of the lie he had told Mary – if it was a lie. After much reflection – suppose it *was* a lie? What then? Was it such a great matter? Aren't we always *acting* lies? Then why not *tell* them? Look at Mary – look what she had done. While he was hurrying off on his honest errand, what was she doing? Lamenting because the papers hadn't been destroyed and the money kept! Is theft better than lying?

That point lost its sting – the lie dropped into the background and left comfort behind it. The next point came to the front: *Had* he rendered that service? Well, here was Goodson's own evidence as reported in Stephenson's letter; there could be no better evidence than that – it was even *proof* that he had rendered it. Of course. So that point was settled . . . No, not quite. He recalled with a wince that this unknown Mr Stephenson was just a trifle unsure as to whether the performer of it was Richards or some other – and, oh dear, he had put Richards on his honor! He must himself decide whither that money must go – and Mr Stephenson was not doubting that if he was the wrong man he would go honorably and find the right one. Oh, it was odious to put a man in such a situation – ah, why couldn't Stephenson have left out that doubt! What did he want to intrude that for?

Further reflection. How did it happen that *Richards's* name remained in Stephenson's mind as indicating the right man, and not some other man's name? That looked good. Yes, that looked very good. In fact, it went on looking better and better, straight along – until by and by it grew into positive *proof*. And then Richards put the matter at once out of his mind, for he had a private instinct that a proof once established is better left so.

He was feeling reasonably comfortable now, but there was still one other detail that kept pushing itself on his notice: of course he had done that service – that was settled; but what *was* that service? He must recall it – he would not go to sleep till he had recalled it; it would make his peace of mind perfect. And so he thought and thought. He thought of a dozen things – possible services, even probable services – but none of them seemed adequate, none of them seemed large enough, none of them seemed worth the money – worth the fortune Goodson had wished he could leave in his will. And besides, he couldn't remember having done them, anyway. Now, then – now, then – what *kind* of a service would it be that would make a man so inordinately grateful? Ah – the saving of his soul! That must be it. Yes, he could remember, now, how he once set himself the task of converting Goodson, and labored at it as much as – he was going to say three months; but upon closer examination it shrunk to a month, then to a week, then to a day, then to nothing. Yes, he remembered now, and with unwelcome vividness, that Goodson had told him to go to thunder and mind his own business – *he* wasn't hankering to follow Hadleyburg to heaven!

So that solution was a failure – he hadn't saved Goodson's soul. Richards was discouraged. Then after a little came another idea: had he saved Goodson's property? No, that wouldn't do – he hadn't any. His life? That is it! Of course. Why, he might have thought of it before. This time he was on the right track, sure. His imagination-mill was hard at work in a minute, now.

Thereafter during a stretch of two exhausting hours he was busy saving Goodson's life. He saved it in all kinds of difficult and perilous ways. In every case he got it saved satisfactorily up to a certain point; then, just as he was beginning to get well persuaded that it had really happened, a troublesome detail would turn up which made the whole thing impossible. As in the matter of drowning, for instance. In that case he had swum out and tugged Goodson ashore in an unconscious state with a great crowd looking on and applauding, but when he had got it all thought out and was just beginning to remember all about it, a whole swarm of disqualifying details arrived on the ground: the town would have known of the circumstance, Mary would have known of it, it would glare like a limelight in his own memory instead of being an inconspicuous service which he had possibly rendered 'without knowing its full value'. And at this point he remembered that he couldn't swim, anyway.

Ah – *there* was a point which he had been overlooking from the start: it had to be a service which he had rendered 'possibly without knowing the full value of it'. Why, really, that ought to be an easy hunt – much easier than those others. And sure enough, by and by he found it. Goodson, years and years ago, came near to marrying a very sweet and pretty girl, named Nancy Hewitt, but in some way or other the match had been broken off; the girl died, Goodson remained a bachelor, and by and by became a soured one and a frank despiser of the human species. Soon after the girl's death the village found out, or thought it had found out, that she carried a spoonful of negro blood in her veins. Richards worked at these details a good while, and in the end he thought he remembered things concerning them which must have gotten mislaid in his memory through long neglect. He seemed to dimly remember that it was *he* that found out about the negro blood; that it was he that told the village; that the village told Goodson where they got it; that he thus saved Goodson from marrying the tainted girl; that he had done him this great service 'without knowing the full value of it', in fact without knowing that he *was* doing it; but that Goodson knew the value of it, and what a narrow escape he had had, and so went to his grave grateful to his benefactor and wishing he had a fortune to leave him. It was all clear and simple now, and the more he went over it the more luminous and certain it grew; and at last, when he nestled to sleep satisfied and happy, he remembered the whole thing, just as if it had been yesterday. In fact, he dimly remembered Goodson's *telling* him his gratitude once. Meantime Mary had spent six thousand dollars on a new house for herself and a pair of slippers for her pastor, and then had fallen peacefully to rest.

That same Saturday evening the postman had delivered a letter to each of the other principal citizens – nineteen letters in all. No two of the envelops were alike, and no two of the superscriptions were in the same hand, but the letters inside were just like each other in every detail but one. They were exact copies of the letter received by Richards – handwriting and all – and were all signed by Stephenson, but in place of Richards's name each receiver's own name appeared.

All night long eighteen principal citizens did what their caste-brother Richards was doing at the same time – they put in their energies trying to remember what notable service it was that they had unconsciously done Barclay Goodson. In no case was it a holiday job; still they succeeded.

And while they were at this work, which was difficult, their wives put in the night spending the money, which was easy. During that one night the nineteen wives spent an average of seven thousand dollars each out of the forty thousand in the sack – a hundred and thirty-three thousand altogether.

Next day there was a surprise for Jack Halliday. He noticed that the faces of the nineteen chief citizens and their wives bore that expression of peaceful and holy happiness again. He could not understand it, neither was he able to invent any remarks about it that could damage it or disturb it. And so it was his turn to be dissatisfied with life. His private guesses at the reasons for the happiness failed in all instances, upon examination. When he met Mrs Wilcox and noticed the placid ecstasy in her face, he said to himself, 'Her cat has had kittens' – and went and asked the cook: it was not so; the cook had detected the happiness, but did not know the cause. When Halliday found the duplicate ecstasy in the face of 'Shadbelly' Billson (village nickname), he was sure some neighbor of Billson's had broken his leg, but inquiry showed that this had not happened. The subdued ecstasy in Gregory Yates's face could mean but one thing – he was a mother-in-law short: it was another mistake. 'And Pinkerton – Pinkerton – he has collected ten cents that he thought he was going to lose.' And so on, and so on. In some cases the guesses had to remain in doubt, in the others they proved distinct errors. In the end Halliday said to himself, 'Anyway it foots up that there's nineteen Hadleyburg families temporarily in heaven: I don't know how it happened; I only know Providence is off duty today.'

An architect and builder from the next state had lately ventured to set up a small business in this unpromising village, and his sign had now been hanging out a week. Not a customer yet; he was a discouraged man, and sorry he had come. But his weather changed suddenly now. First one and then another chief citizen's wife said to him privately:

'Come to my house Monday week – but say nothing about it for the present. We think of building.'

He got eleven invitations that day. That night he wrote his daughter and broke off her match with her student. He said she could marry a mile higher than that.

Pinkerton the banker and two or three other well-to-do men planned country-seats – but waited. That kind don't count their chickens until they are hatched.

The Wilsons devised a grand new thing – a fancy-dress ball. They made no actual promises, but told all their acquaintance-ship in confidence that they were thinking the matter over and thought they should give it – 'and if we do, you will be invited, of course.' People were surprised, and said, one to another, 'Why, they are crazy, those poor Wilsons, they can't afford it.' Several among the nineteen said privately to their husbands, 'It is a good idea: we will keep still till their cheap thing is over, then *we* will give one that will make it sick.'

The days drifted along, and the bill of future squanderings rose higher and higher, wilder and wilder, more and more fool-ish and reckless. It began to look as if every member of the nineteen would not only spend his whole forty thousand dollars before receiving-day, but be actually in debt by the time he got the money. In some cases light-headed people did not stop with planning to spend, they really spent – on credit. They bought land, mortgages, farms, speculative stocks, fine clothes, horses, and various other things, paid down the bonus, and made them-selves liable for the rest – at ten days. Presently the sober second thought came, and Halliday noticed that a ghastly anxiety was beginning to show up in a good many faces. Again he was puz-zled, and didn't know what to make of it. 'The Wilcox kittens aren't dead, for they weren't born; nobody's broken a leg; there's no shrinkage in mother-in-laws; *nothing* has happened – it is an unsolvable mystery.'

There was another puzzled man, too – the Rev. Mr Burgess. For days, wherever he went, people seemed to follow him or to be watching out for him; and if he ever found himself in a retired spot, a member of the nineteen would be sure to appear, thrust an envelope privately into his hand, whisper, 'To be opened at the town-hall Friday evening,' then vanish away like a guilty thing. He was expecting that there might be one claimant of the sack – doubtful, however, Goodson being dead – but it never occurred to him that all this crowd might be claimants. When the great Friday came at last, he found that he had nineteen envelopes.

3

The town-hall had never looked finer. The platform at the end of it was backed by a showy draping of flags; at intervals along the walls were festoons of flags; the gallery fronts were clothed in flags; the supporting columns were swathed in flags; all this was to impress the stranger, for he would be there in considerable force, and in a large degree he would be connected with the press. The house was full. The 412 fixed seats were occupied; also the sixty-eight extra chairs which had been packed into the aisles; the steps of the platform were occupied; some distiguished strangers were given seats on the platform; at the horseshoe of tables which fenced the front and sides of the platform sat a strong force of special correspondents who had come from everywhere. It was the best-dressed house the town had ever produced. There were some tolerably expensive toilets there, and in several cases the ladies who wore them had the look of being unfamiliar with that kind of clothes. At least the town thought they had that look, but the notion could have arisen from the town's knowledge of the fact that these ladies had never inhabited such clothes before.

The gold-sack stood on a little table at the front of the platform where all the house could see it. The bulk of the house gazed at it with a burning interest, a mouth-watering interest, a wistful and pathetic interest; a minority of nineteen couples gazed at it tenderly, lovingly, proprietarily, and the male half of this minority kept saying over to themselves the moving little impromptu speeches of thankfulness for the audience's applause and congratulations which they were presently going to get up and deliver. Every now and then one of these got a piece of paper out of his vest pocket and privately glanced at it to refresh his memory.

Of course there was a buzz of conversation going on – there always is; but at last when the Rev. Mr Burgess rose and laid his hand on the sack he could hear his microbes gnaw, the place was so still. He related the curious history of the sack, then went on to speak in warm terms of Hadleyburg's old and well-earned reputation for spotless honesty, and of the town's just pride in this reputation. He said that this reputation was a treasure of priceless value; that under Providence its value had now become inestimably enhanced, for the recent episode had spread this fame far and wide, and thus had focused the eyes of the American world upon this village, and made its name for all time, as he hoped and believed, a synonym for commercial incorruptibility. [*Applause.*] 'And who is to be the guardian of this noble treasure – the community as a whole? No! The responsibility is individual, not communal. From this day forth each and every one of you is in his own person its special guardian, and individually responsible that no harm shall come to it. Do you – does each of you – accept this great trust? [*Tumultuous assent.*] Then all is well. Transmit it to your children and to your children's children. Today your purity is beyond reproach – see to it that it shall remain so. Today there is not a person in your community who could be beguiled to touch a penny not his own – see to it that you abide in this grace. ['We will! we will!'] This is not the place to make comparisons between ourselves and other communities – some of them ungracious toward us; they have their ways, we have ours; let us be content. [*Applause.*] I am done. Under my hand, my friends, rests a stranger's eloquent recognition of what we are; through him the world will always henceforth know what we are. We do not know who he is, but in your name I utter your gratitude, and ask you to raise your voices in endorsement.'

The house rose in a body and made the walls quake with the thunders of its thankfulness for the space of a long minute. Then it sat down, and Mr Burgess took an envelope out of his pocket. The house held its breath while he slit the envelope open and took from it a slip of paper. He read its contents – slowly and impressively – the audience listening with tranced attention to this magic document, each of whose words stood for an ingot of gold:

'The remark which I made to the distressed stranger was this: "You are very far from being a bad man: go, and reform." ' Then he continued:

'We shall know in a moment now whether the remark here quoted corresponds with the one concealed in the sack; and if that shall prove to be so – and it undoubtedly will – this sack of gold belongs to a fellow-citizen who will henceforth stand before the nation as the symbol of the special virtue which has made our town famous throughout the land – Mr Billson!'

The house had gotten itself all ready to burst into the proper tornado of applause; but instead of doing it, it seemed stricken with a paralysis; there was a deep hush for a moment or two, then a wave of whispered murmurs swept the place – of about this tenor: '*Billson!* oh, come, this is *too* thin! Twenty dollars to a stranger – or *anybody* – Billson! tell it to the marines!' And now at this point the house caught its breath all of a sudden in a new access of astonishment, for it discovered that whereas in one part of the hall Deacon Billson was standing up with his head meekly bowed, in another part of it Lawyer Wilson was doing the same. There was a wondering silence now for a while.

Everybody was puzzled, and nineteen couples were surprised and indignant.

Billson and Wilson turned and stared at each other. Billson asked, bitingly:

'Why do *you* rise, Mr Wilson?'

'Because I have a right to. Perhaps you will be good enough to explain to the house why *you* rise?'

'With great pleasure. Because I wrote that paper.'

'It is an impudent falsity! I wrote it myself.'

It was Burgess's turn to be paralyzed. He stood looking vacantly at first one of the men and then the other, and did not seem to know what to do. The house was stupefied. Lawyer Wilson spoke up, now, and said,

'I ask the Chair to read the name signed to that paper.'

That brought the Chair to itself, and it read out the name:

'John Wharton *Billson*.'

'There!' shouted Billson, 'what have you got to say for yourself, now? And what kind of apology are you going to make to me and to this insulted house for the imposture which you have attempted to play here?'

'No apologies are due, sir; and as for the rest of it, I publicly charge you with pilfering my note from Mr Burgess and substituting a copy of it signed with your own name. There is no other way by which you could have gotten hold of the test-remark; I alone, of living men, possessed the secret of its wording.'

There was likely to be a scandalous state of things if this went on; everybody noticed with distress that the shorthand scribes were scribbling like mad; many people were crying 'Chair, Chair! Order! order!' Burgess rapped with his gavel, and said:

'Let us not forget the proprieties due. There has evidently been a mistake somewhere, but surely that is all. If Mr Wilson gave me an envelope – and I remember now that he did – I still have it.'

He took one out of his pocket, opened it, glanced at it, looked surprised and worried, and stood silent a few moments. Then he waved his hand in a wandering and mechanical way, and made an effort or two to say something, then gave it up, despondently. Several voices cried out:

'Read it! read it! What is it?'

So he began in a dazed and sleep-walker fashion:

'*The remark which I made to the unhappy stranger was this: "You are far from being a bad man.* [The house gazed at him, marveling.] *Go, and reform."* [MURMURS: 'Amazing! what can this mean?'] This one', said the Chair, 'is signed Thurlow G. Wilson.'

'There!' cried Wilson. 'I reckon that settles it! I knew perfectly well my note was purloined.'

'Purloined!' retorted Billson. 'I'll let you know that neither you nor any man of your kidney must venture to—'

THE CHAIR: 'Order, gentlemen, order! Take your seats, both of you, please.'

They obeyed, shaking their heads and grumbling angrily. The house was profoundly puzzled; it did not know what to do with this curious emergency. Presently Thompson got up. Thompson was the hatter. He would have liked to be a Nineteener; but such was not for him: his stock of hats was not considerable enough for the position. He said:

'Mr Chairman, if I may be permitted to make a suggestion, can both of these gentlemen be right? I put it to you, sir, can both have happened to say the very same words to the stranger? It seems to me—'

The tanner got up and interrupted him. The tanner was a disgruntled man; he believed himself entitled to be a Nineteener, but he couldn't get recognition. It made him a little unpleasant in his ways and speech. Said he:

'Sho, *that's* not the point! *That* could happen – twice in a hundred years – but not the other thing. *Neither* of them gave the twenty dollars!'

[*A ripple of applause.*]

BILLSON: '*I* did!'

WILSON: '*I* did!'

Then each accused the other of pilfering.

THE CHAIR: 'Order! Sit down, if you please – both of you. Neither of the notes has been out of my possession at any moment.'

A VOICE: 'Good – that settles *that!*'

THE TANNER: 'Mr Chairman, one thing is now plain: one of these men has been eavesdropping under the other one's bed, and filching family secrets. If it is not unparliamentary to suggest it, I will remark that both are equal to it. [THE CHAIR: 'Order! order!'] I withdraw the remark, sir, and will confine myself to suggesting that *if* one of them has overheard the other reveal the test-remark to his wife, we shall catch him now.'

A VOICE: 'How?'

THE TANNER: 'Easily. The two have not quoted the remark in exactly the same words. You would have noticed that, if there hadn't been a considerable stretch of time and an exciting quarrel inserted between the two readings.'

A VOICE: 'Name the difference.'

THE TANNER: 'The word *very* is in Billson's note, and not in the other.'

MANY VOICES: 'That's so – he's right!'

THE TANNER: 'And so, if the Chair will examine the test-remark in the sack, we shall know which of these two frauds – [THE CHAIR: 'Order!'] – which of these two adventurers – [THE CHAIR: 'Order! order!'] – which of these two gentlemen – [*laughter and applause*] – is entitled to wear the bell as being the first dishonest blatherskite ever bred in this town – which he has dishonored, and which will be a sultry place for him from now out!' [*Vigorous applause.*]

MANY VOICES: 'Open it! – open the sack!'

Mr Burgess made a slit in the sack, slid his hand in and brought out an envelope. In it were a couple of folded notes. He said:

'One of these is marked, *Not to be examined until all written communications which have been addressed to the Chair – if any – shall have been read.* The other is marked *The Test*. Allow me. It is worded – to wit:

'*I do not require that the first half of the remark which was made to me by my benefactor shall be quoted with exactness, for it was not striking, and could be forgotten; but its closing fifteen words are quite striking, and I think easily rememberable; unless these shall be accurately reproduced, let the applicant be regarded as an impostor. My benefactor began by saying he seldom gave advice to anyone, but that it always bore the hallmark of high value when he did give it. Then he said this – and it has never faded from my memory: "You are far from being a bad man—"* '

FIFTY VOICES: 'That settles it – the money's Wilson's! Wilson! Wilson! Speech! Speech!'

People jumped up and crowded around Wilson, wringing his hand and congratulating fervently – meantime the Chair was hammering with the gavel and shouting:

'Order, gentlemen! Order! Order! Let me finish reading, please.' When quiet was restored, the reading was resumed – as follows:

' "*Go, and reform – or, mark my words – some day, for your sins, you will die and go to Hell or Hadleyburg –* TRY AND MAKE IT THE FORMER." '

A ghastly silence followed. First an angry cloud began to settle darkly upon the faces of the citizenship; after a pause the cloud began to rise, and a tickled expression tried to take its place; tried so hard that it was only kept under with great and painful difficulty; the reporters, the Brixtonites, and other strangers bent their heads down and shielded their faces with their hands, and managed to hold in by main strength and heroic courtesy. At this most inopportune time burst upon the stillness the roar of a solitary voice – Jack Halliday's:

'That's got the hallmark on it!'

Then the house let go, strangers and all. Even Mr Burgess's gravity broke down presently, then the audience considered itself officially absolved from all restraint, and it made the most of its privilege. It was a good long laugh, and a tempestuously whole-hearted one, but it ceased at last – long enough for Mr

Burgess to try to resume, and for the people to get their eyes partially wiped; then it broke out again; and afterward yet again; then at last Burgess was able to get out these serious words:

'It is useless to try to disguise the fact – we find ourselves in the presence of a matter of grave import. It involves the honor of your town, it strikes at the town's good name. The difference of a single word between the test-remarks offered by Mr Wilson and Mr Billson was itself a serious thing, since it indicated that one or the other of these gentlemen had committed a theft—'

The two men were sitting limp, nerveless, crushed; but at these words both were electrified into movement, and started to get up—

'Sit down!' said the Chair, sharply, and they obeyed. 'That, as I have said, was a serious thing. And it was – but for only one of them. But the matter has become graver; for the honor of *both* is now in formidable peril. Shall I go even further, and say in inextricable peril? *Both* left out the crucial fifteen words.' He paused. During several moments he allowed the pervading stillness to gather and deepen its impressive effects, then added: 'There would seem to be but one way whereby this could happen. I ask these gentlemen – Was there *collusion? – agreement?*'

A low murmur sifted through the house; its import was, 'He's got them both.'

Billson was not used to emergencies; he sat in a helpless collapse. But Wilson was a lawyer. He struggled to his feet, pale and worried, and said:

'I ask the indulgence of the house while I explain this most painful matter. I am sorry to say what I am about to say, since it must inflict irreparable injury upon Mr Billson, whom I have always esteemed and respected until now, and in whose invulnerability to temptation I entirely believed – as did you all. But for the preservation of my own honor I must speak – and with frankness. I confess with shame – and I now beseech your pardon for it – that I said to the ruined stranger all of the words contained in the test-remark, including the disparaging fifteen. [*Sensation.*] When the late publication was made I recalled them, and I resolved to claim the sack of coin, for by every right I was entitled to it. Now I will ask you to consider this point, and weigh it well: that stranger's gratitude to me that night knew no bounds; he said himself that he could find no words for it that were adequate, and that if he should ever be able he would repay me a thousandfold. Now, then, I ask you this: Could I expect – could I believe – could I even remotely imagine – that, feeling as he did, he would do so ungrateful a thing as to add those quite unnecessary fifteen words to his test? – set a trap for me? – expose me as a slanderer of my own town before my own people assembled in a public hall? It was preposterous; it was impossible. His test would contain only the kindly opening clause of my remark. Of that I had no shadow of doubt. You would have thought as I did. You would not have expected a base betrayal from one whom you had befriended and against whom you had committed no offense. And so, with perfect confidence, perfect trust, I wrote on a piece of paper the opening words – ending with "Go, and reform," – and signed it. When I was about to put it in an envelope I was called into my back office, and without thinking I left the paper lying open on my desk.' He stopped, turned his head slowly toward Billson, waited a moment, then added: 'I ask you to note this: when I returned, a little later, Mr Billson was retiring by my street door.' [*Sensation.*]

In a moment Billson was on his feet and shouting:

'It's a lie! It's an infamous lie!'

THE CHAIR: 'Be seated, sir! Mr Wilson has the floor.'

Billson's friends pulled him into his seat and quieted him, and Wilson went on:

'Those are the simple facts. My note was now lying in a different place on the table from where I had left it. I noticed that, but attached no importance to it, thinking a draft had blown it there. That Mr Billson would read a private paper was a thing which could not occur to me; he was an honorable man, and he would be above that. If you will allow me to say it, I think his extra word "*very*" stands explained; it is attributable to a defect of memory. I was the only man in the world who could furnish here any detail of the test-remark – by *honorable* means. I have finished.'

There is nothing in the world like a persuasive speech to fuddle the mental apparatus and upset the convictions and debauch the emotions of an audience not practiced in the tricks and delusions of oratory. Wilson sat down victorious. The house submerged him in tides of approving applause; friends swarmed to him and shook him by the hand and congratulated him, and Billson was shouted down and not allowed to say a word. The Chair hammered and hammered with its gavel, and kept shouting:

'But let us proceed, gentlemen, let us proceed!'

At last there was a measurable degree of quiet, and the hatter said:

'But what is there to proceed with, sir, but to deliver the money?'

VOICES: 'That's it! That's it! Come forward, Wilson!'

THE HATTER: 'I move three cheers for Mr Wilson, Symbol of the special virtue which—'

The cheers burst forth before he could finish; and in the midst of them – and in the midst of the clamor of the gavel also – some enthusiasts mounted Wilson on a big friend's shoulder and were going to fetch him in triumph to the platform. The Chair's voice now rose above the noise.

'Order! To your places! You forget that there is still a document to be read.' When quiet had been restored he took up the document, and was going to read it, but laid it down again, saying, 'I forgot: this is not to be read until all written communications received by me have first been read.' He took an envelope out of his pocket, removed its enclosure, glanced at it – seemed astonished – held it out and gazed at it – stared at it.

Twenty or thirty voices cried out:

'What is it? Read it! read it!'

And he did – slowly, and wondering:

'*The remark which I made to the stranger –* [VOICES: 'Hallo! how's this?'] – *was this: 'You are far from being a bad man.* [VOICES: 'Great Scott!'] *Go, and reform.'* [VOICES: 'Oh, saw my leg off!'] Signed by Mr Pinkerton, the banker.'

The pandemonium of delight which turned itself loose now was of a sort to make the judicious weep. Those whose withers were unwrung laughed till the tears ran down; the reporters, in throes of laughter, set down disordered pothooks which would never in the world be decipherable; and a sleeping dog jumped up, scared out of its wits, and barked itself crazy at the turmoil. All manner of cries were scattered through the din:

'We're getting rich – *two* Symbols of Incorruptibility! – without counting Billson!' '*Three!* – count Shadbelly in – we can't have too many!' 'All right – Billson's elected!' 'Alas, poor Wilson – victim of *two* thieves!'

A POWERFUL VOICE: 'Silence! The Chair's fished up something more out of its pocket.'

VOICES: 'Hurrah! Is it something fresh? Read it! read! read!'

THE CHAIR [*reading*]: '*The remark which I made*, etc.: "*You are far from being a bad man. Go*", etc. Signed, Gregory Yates.'

TORNADO OF VOICES: 'Four Symbols!' ' 'Rah for Yates!' 'Fish again!'

The house was in a roaring humor now, and ready to get all the fun out of the occasion that might be in it. Several Nineteeners, looking pale and distressed, got up and began to work their way toward the aisles, but a score of shouts went up:

'The doors, the doors – close the doors; no Incorruptible shall leave this place! Sit down, everybody!'

The mandate was obeyed.

'Fish again! Read! read!'

The Chair fished again, and once more the familiar words began to fall from its lips – '*You are far from being a bad man.*'

'Name! name! What's his name?'

'L. Ingoldsby Sargent.'

'Five elected! Pile up the Symbols! Go on, go on!'

'*You are far from being a bad—* '

'Name! name!'

'Nicholas Whitworth.'

'Hooray! hooray! it's a symbolical day!'

Somebody wailed in, and began to sing this rhyme (leaving out 'it's') to the lovely *Mikado* tune of 'When a man's afraid, a beautiful maid'; the audience joined in, with joy; then, just in time, somebody contributed another line –

And don't you this forget –

The house roared it out. A third line was at once furnished –

Corruptibles far from Hadleyburg are –

The house roared that one too. As the last note died, Jack Halliday's voice rose high and clear, freighted with a final line –

But the Symbols are here, you bet!

That was sung, with booming enthusiasm. Then the happy house started in at the beginning and sang the four lines through twice, with immense swing and dash, and finished up with a crashing three-times-three and a tiger for 'Hadleyburg the Incorruptible and all Symbols of it which we shall find worthy to receive the hallmark tonight'.

Then the shoutings at the Chair began again, all over the place:

'Go on! go on! Read! read some more! Read all you've got!'

'That's it – go on! We are winning eternal celebrity!'

A dozen men got up now and began to protest. They said that this farce was the work of some abandoned joker, and was an insult to the whole community. Without a doubt these signatures were all forgeries—

'Sit down! sit down! Shut up! You are confessing. We'll find *your* names in the lot.'

'Mr Chairman, how many of those envelopes have you got?'

The Chair counted.

'Together with those that have been already examined, there are nineteen.'

A storm of derisive applause broke out.

'Perhaps they all contain the secret. I move that you open them all and read every signature that is attached to a note of that sort – and read also the first eight words of the note.'

'Second the motion!'

It was put and carried – uproariously. Then poor old Richards got up, and his wife rose and stood at his side. Her head was bent down, so that none might see that she was crying. Her husband gave her his arm, and so supporting her, he began to speak in a quavering voice:

'My friends, you have known us two – Mary and me – all our lives, and I think you have liked us and respected us—'

The Chair interrupted him:

'Allow me. It is quite true – that which you are saying, Mr Richards: this town *does* know you two; it *does* like you; it *does* respect you; more – it honors you and *loves* you—'

Halliday's voice rang out:

'That's the hallmarked truth, too! If the Chair is right, let the house speak up and say it. Rise! Now, then – hip! hip! hip! – all together!'

The house rose in mass, faced toward the old couple eagerly, filled the air with a snow-storm of waving handkerchiefs, and delivered the cheers with all its affectionate heart.

The Chair then continued:

'What I was going to say is this: We know your good heart, Mr Richards, but this is not a time for the exercise of charity toward offenders. [*Shouts of 'Right! right!'*] I see your generous purpose in your face, but I cannot allow you to plead for these men—'

'But I was going to—'

'Please take your seat, Mr Richards. We must examine the rest of these notes – simple fairness to the men who have already been exposed requires this. As soon as that has been done – I give you my word for this – you shall be heard.'

MANY VOICES: 'Right! – the Chair is right – no interruption can be permitted at this stage! Go on! – the names! the names! – according to the terms of the motion!'

The old couple sat reluctantly down, and the husband whispered to the wife, 'It is pitifully hard to have to wait; the shame will be greater than ever when they find we were only going to plead for *ourselves*.'

Straightway the jollity broke loose again with the reading of the names.

'*You are far from being a bad man*— Signature, Robert J. Titmarsh.'

'*You are far from being a bad man*— Signature, Eliphalet Weeks.'

'*You are far from being a bad man*— Signature, Oscar B. Wilder.'

At this point the house lit upon the idea of taking the eight words out of the Chairman's hands. He was not unthankful for that. Thenceforward he held up each note in its turn, and waited. The house droned out the eight words in a massed and measured and musical deep volume of sound (with a daringly close resemblance to a well-known church chant) – '*You are*

f-a-r from being a b-a-a-a-d man.' Then the Chair said, 'Signature, Archibald Wilcox.' And so on, and so on, name after
name, and everybody had an increasingly and gloriously good
time except the wretched Nineteen. Now and then, when a particularly shining name was called, the house made the Chair
wait while it chanted the whole of the test-remark from the
beginning to the closing words, '*And go to Hell or Hadleyburg –
try and make it the for-or-m-e-r!*' and in these special cases they
added a grand and agonized and imposing 'A-a-a-a-men!'

The list dwindled, dwindled, dwindled, poor old Richards
keeping tally of the count, wincing when a name resembling his
own was pronounced, and waiting in miserable suspense for the
time to come when it would be his humiliating privilege to rise
with Mary and finish his plea, which he was intending to word
thus: '. . . for until now we have never done any wrong thing,
but have gone our humble way unreproached. We are very poor,
we are old, and have no chick nor child to help us; we were
sorely tempted, and we fell. It was my purpose when I got up
before to make confession and beg that my name might not be
read out in this public place, for it seemed to us that we could
not bear it; but I was prevented. It was just; it was our place to
suffer with the rest. It has been hard for us. It is the first time we
have ever heard our name fall from anyone's lips – sullied. Be
merciful – for the sake of the better days; make our shame as
light to bear as in your charity you can.' At this point in his
revery Mary nudged him, perceiving that his mind was absent.
The house was chanting, '*You are f-a-r*', etc.

'Be ready,' Mary whispered. 'Your name comes now; he has
read eighteen.'

The chant ended.

'Next! next! next!' came volleying from all over the house.

Burgess put his hand into his pocket. The old couple, trembling, began to rise. Burgess fumbled a moment, then said,

'I find I have read them all.'

Faint with joy and surprise, the couple sank into their seats,
and Mary whispered:

'Oh, bless God, we are saved! – he has lost ours – I wouldn't
give this for a hundred of those sacks!'

The house burst out with its *Mikado* travesty, and sang it

three times with ever-increasing enthusiasm, rising to its feet when it reached for the third time the closing line –

> But the Symbols are here, you bet!

and finishing up with cheers and a tiger for 'Hadleyburg purity and our eighteen immortal representatives of it'.

Then Wingate, the saddler, got up and proposed cheers 'for the cleanest man in town, the one solitary important citizen in it who didn't try to steal that money – Edward Richards'.

They were given with great and moving heartiness; then somebody proposed that Richards be elected sole guardian and Symbol of the now Sacred Hadleyburg Tradition, with power and right to stand up and look the whole sarcastic world in the face.

Passed, by acclamation; then they sang the *Mikado* again, and ended it with:

> And there's one Symbol left, you bet!

There was a pause; then –

A VOICE: 'Now, then, who's to get the sack?'

THE TANNER [*with bitter sarcasm*]: 'That's easy. The money has to be divided among the eighteen Incorruptibles. They gave the suffering stranger twenty dollars apiece – and that remark – each in his turn – it took twenty-two minutes for the procession to move past. Staked the stranger – total contribution, $360. All they want is just the loan back – and interest – forty thousand dollars altogether.'

MANY VOICES [*derisively*]: 'That's it! Divvy! divvy! Be kind to the poor – don't keep them waiting!'

THE CHAIR: 'Order! I now offer the stranger's remaining document. It says: *If no claimant shall appear* [*grand chorus of groans*] *I desire that you open the sack and count out the money to the principal citizens of your town, they to take it in trust* [*cries of 'Oh! Oh! Oh!'*], *and use it in such ways as to them shall seem best for the propagation and preservation of your community's noble reputation for incorruptible honesty* [*more cries*] *– a reputation to which their names and their efforts will add a new and far-reaching luster.* [*Enthusiastic outburst of sarcastic applause.*] That seems to be all. No – here is a postscript:

PS – CITIZENS OF HADLEYBURG: *There is no test-remark –* *nobody made one.* [*Great sensation.*] *There wasn't any pauper* *stranger, nor any twenty-dollar contribution, nor any accompanying* *benediction and compliment – these are all inventions.* [*General buzz* *and hum of astonishment and delight.*] *Allow me to tell my story – it* *will take but a word or two. I passed through your town at a certain* *time, and received a deep offense which I had not earned. Any other* *man would have been content to kill one or two of you and call it* *square, but to me that would have been a trivial revenge, and inad-* *equate; for the dead do not suffer. Besides, I could not kill you all –* *and, anyway, made as I am, even that would not have satisfied me. I* *wanted to damage every man in the place, and every woman – and* *not in their bodies or in their estate, but in their vanity – the place* *where feeble and foolish people are most vulnerable. So I disguised* *myself and came back and studied you. You were easy game. You had* *an old and lofty reputation for honesty, and naturally you were proud* *of it – it was your treasure of treasures, the very apple of your eye. As* *soon as I found out that you carefully and vigilantly kept yourselves* *and your children out of temptation, I knew how to proceed. Why,* *you simple creatures, the weakest of all weak things is a virtue which* *has not been tested in the fire. I laid a plan, and gathered a list of* *names. My project was to corrupt Hadleyburg the Incorruptible. My* *idea was to make liars and thieves of nearly half a hundred smirchless* *men and women who had never in their lives uttered a lie or stolen* *a penny. I was afraid of Goodson. He was neither born nor reared* *in Hadleyburg. I was afraid that if I started to operate my scheme* *by getting my letter laid before you, you would say to yourselves,* "*Goodson is the only man among us who would give away twenty* *dollars to a poor devil*" *– and then you might not bite at my bait. But* *Heaven took Goodson; then I knew I was safe, and I set my trap and* *baited it. It may be that I shall not catch all the men to whom I mailed* *the pretended test-secret, but I shall catch the most of them, if I know* *Hadleyburg nature.* [VOICES: 'Right – he got every last one of them.'] *I believe they will even steal ostensible gamble-money,* *rather than miss, poor, tempted, and mistrained fellows. I am hoping* *to eternally and everlastingly squelch your vanity and give Hadley-* *burg a new renown – one that will* stick *– and spread far. If I have* *succeeded, open the sack and summon the Committee on Propaga-* *tion and Preservation of the Hadleyburg Reputation!*'

A CYCLONE OF VOICES: 'Open it! Open it! The Eighteen to the front! Committee on Propagation of the Tradition! Forward – the Incorruptibles!'

The Chair ripped the sack wide, and gathered up a handful of bright, broad, yellow coins, shook them together, then examined them –

'Friends, they are only gilded disks of lead!'

There was a crashing outbreak of delight over this news, and when the noise had subsided, the tanner called out:

'By right of apparent seniority in this business, Mr Wilson is Chairman of the Committee on Propagation of the Tradition. I suggest that he step forward on behalf of his pals, and receive in trust the money.'

A HUNDRED VOICES: 'Wilson! Wilson! Wilson! Speech! Speech!'

WILSON [*in a voice trembling with anger*]: 'You will allow me to say, and without apologies for my language, *damn* the money!'

A VOICE: 'Oh, and him a Baptist!'

A VOICE: 'Seventeen Symbols left! Step up, gentlemen, and assume your trust!'

There was a pause – no response.

THE SADDLER: 'Mr Chairman, we've got *one* clean man left, anyway, out of the late aristocracy; and he needs money, and deserves it. I move that you appoint Jack Halliday to get up there and auction off that sack of gilt twenty-dollar pieces, and give the result to the right man – the man whom Hadleyburg delights to honor – Edward Richards.'

This was received with great enthusiasm, the dog taking a hand again; the saddler started the bids at a dollar, the Brixton folk and Barnum's representative fought hard for it, the people cheered every jump that the bids made, the excitement climbed moment by moment higher and higher, the bidders got on their mettle and grew steadily more and more daring, more and more determined, the jumps went from a dollar up to five, then to ten, then to twenty, then fifty, then to a hundred, then—

At the beginning of the auction Richards whispered in distress to his wife: 'O Mary, can we allow it? It – it – you see, it is an honor-reward, a testimonial to purity of character, and – and – can we allow it? Hadn't I better get up and— O Mary, what ought we to do? – what do you think we—' [HALLIDAY'S VOICE: 'Fifteen I'm bid! – fifteen for the sack! – twenty! – ah, thanks! – thirty – thanks again! Thirty, thirty, thirty! – do I hear forty? – forty it is! Keep the ball rolling, gentlemen, keep it rolling! – fifty! thanks, noble Roman! going at fifty, fifty, fifty! – seventy! – ninety! – splendid! – a hundred! – pile it up, pile it up! – hundred and twenty – forty! – just in time! – hundred and fifty! – TWO hundred! – superb! Do I hear two h— thanks! – two hundred and fifty! – ']

'It is another temptation, Edward – I'm all in a tremble – but, oh, we've escaped *one* temptation, and that ought to warn us to— ['Six did I hear? – thanks! – six-fifty, six-f— SEVEN hundred!'] And yet, Edward, when you think – nobody susp— ['Eight hundred dollars! – hurrah! – make it nine! – Mr Parsons, did I hear you say – thanks – nine! – this noble sack of virgin lead going at only nine hundred dollars, gilding and all – come! do I hear – a thousand! – gratefully yours! – did someone say eleven? – a sack which is going to be the most celebrated in the whole Uni—'] O Edward' (beginning to sob), 'we are *so* poor! – but – but – do as you think best – do as you think best.'

Edward fell – that is, he sat still; sat with a conscience which was not satisfied, but which was overpowered by circumstances.

Meantime a stranger, who looked like an amateur detective gotten up as an impossible English earl, had been watching the evening's proceedings with manifest interest, and with a contented expression in his face; and he had been privately commenting to himself. He was now soliloquizing somewhat like this: 'None of the Eighteen are bidding; that is not satisfactory; I must change that – the dramatic unities require it; they must buy the sack they tried to steal; they must pay a heavy price, too – some of them are rich. And another thing, when I make a mistake in Hadleyburg nature the man that puts that error upon me is entitled to a high honorarium, and someone must pay it. This poor old Richards has brought my judgment to shame; he is an honest man: I don't understand it, but I acknowledge it. Yes, he saw my deuces *and* with a straight flush, and by rights the pot is his. And it shall be a jackpot, too, if I can manage it. He disappointed me, but let that pass.'

He was watching the bidding. At a thousand, the market

broke; the prices tumbled swiftly. He waited – and still watched. One competitor dropped out; then another, and another. He put in a bid or two, now. When the bids had sunk to ten dollars, he added a five; someone raised him a three; he waited a moment, then flung in a fifty-dollar jump, and the sack was his – at $1,282. The house broke out in cheers – then stopped; for he was on his feet, and had lifted his hand. He began to speak.

'I desire to say a word, and ask a favor. I am a speculator in rarities, and I have dealings with persons interested in numismatics all over the world. I can make a profit on this purchase, just as it stands; but there is a way, if I can get your approval, whereby I can make every one of these leaden twenty-dollar pieces worth its face in gold, and perhaps more. Grant me that approval, and I will give part of my gains to your Mr Richards, whose invulnerable probity you have so justly and so cordially recognized tonight; his share shall be ten thousand dollars, and I will hand him the money tomorrow. [*Great applause from the house.* But the 'invulnerable probity' made the Richardses blush prettily; however, it went for modesty, and did no harm.] If you will pass my proposition by a good majority – I would like a two-thirds vote – I will regard that as the town's consent, and that is all I ask. Rarities are always helped by any device which will rouse curiosity and compel remark. Now if I may have your permission to stamp upon the faces of each of these ostensible coins the names of the eighteen gentlemen who—'

Nine-tenths of the audience were on their feet in a moment – dog and all – and the proposition was carried with a whirlwind of approving applause and laughter.

They sat down, and all the Symbols except 'Dr' Clay Harkness got up, violently protesting against the proposed outrage, and threatening to—

'I beg you not to threaten me,' said the stranger, calmly. 'I know my legal rights, and am not accustomed to being frightened at bluster.' [*Applause.*] He sat down. 'Dr' Harkness saw an opportunity here. He was one of the two very rich men of the place, and Pinkerton was the other. Harkness was proprietor of a mint; that is to say, a popular patent medicine. He was running for the legislature on one ticket, and Pinkerton on the other. It was a close race and a hot one, and getting hotter every day. Both had strong appetites for money; each had bought a great tract of land, with a purpose; there was going to be a new railway, and each wanted to be in the legislature and help locate the route to his own advantage; a single vote might make the decision, and with it two or three fortunes. The stake was large, and Harkness was a daring speculator. He was sitting close to the stranger. He leaned over while one or another of the other Symbols was entertaining the house with protests and appeals, and asked, in a whisper:

'What is your price for the sack?'

'Forty thousand dollars.'

'I'll give you twenty.'

'No.'

'Twenty-five.'

'No.'

'Say thirty.'

'The price is forty thousand dollars; not a penny less.'

'All right, I'll give it. I will come to the hotel at ten in the morning. I don't want it known: will see you privately.'

'Very good.' Then the stranger got up and said to the house:

'I find it late. The speeches of these gentlemen are not without merit, not without interest, not without grace; yet if I may be excused I will take my leave. I thank you for the great favor which you have shown me in granting my petition. I ask the Chair to keep the sack for me until tomorrow, and to hand these three five-hundred-dollar notes to Mr Richards.' They were passed up to the Chair. 'At nine I will call for the sack, and at eleven will deliver the rest of the ten thousand to Mr Richards in person, at his home. Good night.'

Then he slipped out, and left the audience making a vast noise, which was composed of a mixture of cheers, the *Mikado* song, dog-disapproval, and the chant, '*You are f-a-r from being a b-a-a-d man – A-a-a-a-men!*'

4

At home the Richardses had to endure congratulations and compliments until midnight. Then they were left to themselves. They looked a little sad, and they sat silent and thinking. Finally Mary sighed and said,

'Do you think we are to blame, Edward – *much* to blame?' and her eyes wandered to the accusing triplet of big bank-notes lying on the table, where the congratulators had been gloating over them and reverently fingering them. Edward did not answer at once; then he brought out a sigh and said, hesitatingly:

'We – we couldn't help it, Mary. It – well, it was ordered. *All* things are.'

Mary glanced up and looked at him steadily, but he didn't return the look. Presently she said:

'I thought congratulations and praises always tasted good. But – it seems to me, now – Edward?'

'Well?'

'Are you going to stay in the bank?'

'N-no.'

'Resign?'

'In the morning – by note.'

'It does seem best.'

Richards bowed his head in his hands and muttered:

'Before, I was not afraid to let oceans of people's money pour through my hands, but – Mary, I am so tired, so tired—'

'We will go to bed.'

At nine in the morning the stranger called for the sack and took it to the hotel in a cab. At ten Harkness had a talk with him privately. The stranger asked for and got five checks on a metropolitan bank – drawn to 'Bearer' – four for $1,500 each and one for $34,000. He put one of the former in his pocket-book, and the remainder, representing $38,500, he put in an envelope, and with these he added a note, which he wrote after Harkness was gone. At eleven he called at the Richards house and knocked. Mrs Richards peeped through the shutters, then went and received the envelope, and the stranger disappeared without a word. She came back flushed and a little unsteady on her legs, and gasped out:

'I am sure I recognized him! Last night it seemed to me that maybe I had seen him somewhere before.'

'He is the man that brought the sack here?'

'I am almost sure of it.'

'Then he is the ostensible Stephenson, too, and sold every

important citizen in this town with his bogus secret. Now if he has sent checks instead of money, we are sold, too, after we thought we had escaped. I was beginning to feel fairly comfortable once more, after my night's rest, but the look of that envelope makes me sick. It isn't fat enough; $8,500 in even the largest bank-notes makes more bulk than that.'

'Edward, why do you object to checks?'

'Checks signed by Stephenson! I am resigned to take the $8,500 if it could come in bank-notes – for it does seem that it was so ordered, Mary – but I have never had much courage, and I have not the pluck to try to market a check signed with that disastrous name. It would be a trap. That man tried to catch me; we escaped somehow or other; and now he is trying a new way. If it is checks—'

'Oh, Edward, it is *too* bad!' and she held up the checks and began to cry.

'Put them in the fire! quick! we mustn't be tempted. It is a trick to make the world laugh at *us*, along with the rest, and— Give them to *me*, since you can't do it!' He snatched them and tried to hold his grip till he could get to the stove; but he was human, he was a cashier, and he stopped a moment to make sure of the signature. Then he came near to fainting.

'Fan me, Mary, fan me! They are the same as gold!'

'Oh, how lovely, Edward! Why?'

'Signed by Harkness. What can the mystery of that be, Mary?'

'Edward, do you think—'

'Look here – look at this! Fifteen – fifteen – fifteen – thirty-four. Thirty-eight thousand five hundred! Mary, the sack isn't worth twelve dollars, and Harkness – apparently – has paid about par for it.'

'And does it all come to us, do you think – instead of the ten thousand?'

'Why, it looks like it. And the checks are made to "Bearer", too.'

'Is that good, Edward? What is it for?'

'A hint to collect them at some distant bank, I reckon. Perhaps Harkness doesn't want the matter known. What is that – a note?'

'Yes. It was with the checks.'

It was in the 'Stephenson' handwriting, but there was no signature. It said:

I am a disappointed man. Your honesty is beyond the reach of temptation. I had a different idea about it, but I wronged you in that, and I beg pardon, and do it sincerely. I honor you – and that is sincere too. This town is not worthy to kiss the hem of your garment. Dear sir, I made a square bet with myself that there were nineteen debauchable men in your self-righteous community. I have lost. Take the whole pot, you are entitled to it.

Richards drew a deep sigh, and said:
'It seems written with fire – it burns so. Mary – I am miserable again.'
'I, too. Ah, dear, I wish—'
'To think, Mary – he *believes* in me.'
'Oh, don't, Edward – I can't bear it.'
'If those beautiful words were deserved, Mary – and God knows I believed I deserved them once – I think I could give the forty thousand dollars for them. And I would put that paper away, as representing more than gold and jewels, and keep it always. But now— We could not live in the shadow of its accusing presence, Mary.'
He put it in the fire.
A messenger arrived and delivered an envelope.
Richards took from it a note and read it; it was from Burgess.

You saved me, in a difficult time. I saved you last night. It was at cost of a lie, but I made the sacrifice freely, and out of a grateful heart. None in this village knows so well as I know how brave and good and noble you are. At bottom you cannot respect me, knowing as you do of that matter of which I am accused, and by the general voice condemned; but I beg that you will at least believe that I am a grateful man; it will help me to bear my burden.

[Signed] BURGESS

'Saved, once more. And on such terms!' He put the note in

the fire. 'I – I wish I were dead, Mary, I wish I were out of it all.'

'Oh, these are bitter, bitter days, Edward. The stabs, through their very generosity, are so deep – and they come so fast!'

Three days before the election each of two thousand voters suddenly found himself in possession of a prized memento – one of the renowned bogus double-eagles. Around one of its faces was stamped these words: THE REMARK I MADE TO THE POOR STRANGER WAS – Around the other face was stamped these: GO, AND REFORM. [SIGNED] PINKERTON. Thus the entire remaining refuse of the renowned joke was emptied upon a single head, and with calamitous effect. It revived the recent vast laugh and concentrated it upon Pinkerton; and Harkness's election was a walkover.

Within twenty-four hours after the Richardses had received their checks their consciences were quieting down, discouraged; the old couple were learning to reconcile themselves to the sin which they had committed. But they were to learn, now, that a sin takes on new and real terrors when there seems a chance that it is going to be found out. This gives it a fresh and most substantial and important aspect. At church the morning sermon was of the usual pattern; it was the same old things said in the same old way; they had heard them a thousand times and found them innocuous, next to meaningless, and easy to sleep under; but now it was different: the sermon seemed to bristle with accusations; it seemed aimed straight and specially at people who were concealing deadly sins. After church they got away from the mob of congratulators as soon as they could, and hurried homeward, chilled to the bone at they did not know what – vague, shadowy, indefinite fears. And by chance they caught a glimpse of Mr Burgess as he turned a corner. He paid no attention to their nod of recognition! He hadn't seen it; but they did not know that. What could his conduct mean? It might mean – it might mean – oh, a dozen dreadful things. Was it possible that he knew that Richards could have cleared him of guilt in that bygone time, and had been silently waiting for a chance to even up accounts? At home, in their distress they got to imagining that their servant might have been in the next room listening when Richards revealed the secret to his wife that he knew of

Burgess's innocence; next, Richards began to imagine that he had heard the swish of a gown in there at that time; next, he was sure he *had* heard it. They would call Sarah in, on a pretext, and watch her face: if she had been betraying them to Mr Burgess, it would show in her manner. They asked her some questions – questions which were so random and incoherent and seemingly purposeless that the girl felt sure that the old people's minds had been affected by their sudden good fortune; the sharp and watchful gaze which they bent upon her frightened her, and that completed the business. She blushed, she became nervous and confused, and to the old people these were plain signs of guilt – guilt of some fearful sort or other – without doubt she was a spy and a traitor. When they were alone again they began to piece many unrelated things together and get horrible results out of the combination. When things had got about to the worst, Richards was delivered of a sudden gasp, and his wife asked:

'Oh, what is it? – what is it?'

'The note – Burgess's note! Its language was sarcastic, I see it now.' He quoted: ' "At bottom you cannot respect me, *knowing*, as you do, of *that matter* of which I am accused" – oh, it is perfectly plain, now, God help me! He knows that I know! You see the ingenuity of the phrasing. It was a trap – and like a fool, I walked into it. And Mary—?'

'Oh, it is dreadful – I know what you are going to say – he didn't return your transcript of the pretended test-remark.'

'No – kept it to destroy us with. Mary, he has exposed us to some already. I know it – I know it well. I saw it in a dozen faces after church. Ah, he wouldn't answer our nod of recognition – *he* knew what he had been doing!'

In the night the doctor was called. The news went around in the morning that the old couple were rather seriously ill – prostrated by the exhausting excitement growing out of their great windfall, the congratulations, and the late hours, the doctor said. The town was sincerely distressed; for these old people were about all it had left to be proud of, now.

Two days later the news was worse. The old couple were delirious, and were doing strange things. By witness of the nurses, Richards had exhibited checks – for $8,500? No – for an amazing sum – $38,500! What could be the explanation of this gigantic piece of luck?

The following day the nurses had more news – and wonderful. They had concluded to hide the checks, lest harm come to them; but when they searched they were gone from under the patient's pillow – vanished away. The patient said:

'Let the pillow alone; what do you want?'

'We thought it best that the checks—'

'You will never see them again – they are destroyed. They came from Satan. I saw the hell-brand on them, and I knew they were sent to betray me to sin.' Then he fell to gabbling strange and dreadful things which were not clearly understandable, and which the doctor admonished them to keep to themselves.

Richards was right; the checks were never seen again.

A nurse must have talked in her sleep, for within two days the forbidden gabblings were the property of the town; and they were of a surprising sort. They seemed to indicate that Richards had been a claimant for the sack himself, and that Burgess had concealed that fact and then maliciously betrayed it.

Burgess was taxed with this and stoutly denied it. And he said it was not fair to attach weight to the chatter of a sick old man who was out of his mind. Still, suspicion was in the air, and there was much talk.

After a day or two it was reported that Mrs Richards's delirious deliveries were getting to be duplicates of her husband's. Suspicion flamed up into conviction, now, and the town's pride in the purity of its one undiscredited important citizen began to dim down and flicker toward extinction.

Six days passed, then came more news. The old couple were dying. Richards's mind cleared in his latest hour, and he sent for Burgess. Burgess said:

'Let the room be cleared. I think he wishes to say something in privacy.'

'No!' said Richards: 'I want witnesses. I want you all to hear my confession, so that I may die a man, and not a dog. I was clean – artificially – like the rest; and like the rest I fell when temptation came. I signed a lie, and claimed the miserable sack. Mr Burgess remembered that I had done him a service, and in gratitude (and ignorance) he suppressed my claim and saved me. You know the thing that was charged against Burgess years ago. My testimony, and mine alone, could have cleared him, and I was a coward, and left him to suffer disgrace—'

'No – no – Mr Richards, you—'

'My servant betrayed my secret to him—'

'No one has betrayed anything to me—'

'And then he did a natural and justifiable thing, he repented of the saving kindness which he had done me, and he *exposed* me – as I deserved—'

'Never! – I make oath—'

'Out of my heart I forgive him.'

Burgess's impassioned protestations fell upon deaf ears; the dying man passed away without knowing that once more he had done poor Burgess a wrong. The old wife died that night.

The last of the sacred Nineteen had fallen a prey to the fiendish sack; the town was stripped of the last rag of its ancient glory. Its mourning was not showy, but it was deep.

By act of the Legislature – upon prayer and petition – Hadleyburg was allowed to change its name to (never mind what – I will not give it away), and leave one word out of the motto that for many generations had graced the town's official seal.

It is an honest town once more, and the man will have to rise early that catches it napping again.

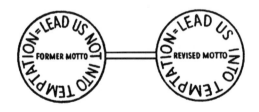

General Washington's Negro Body-Servant

The stirring part of this celebrated colored man's life properly began with his death – that is to say, the notable features of his biography begin with the first time he died. He had been little heard of up to that time, but since then we have never ceased to hear of him; we have never ceased to hear of him at stated, unfailing intervals. His was a most remarkable career, and I have thought that its history would make a valuable addition to our biographical literature. Therefore, I have carefully collated the materials for such a work, from authentic sources, and here present them to the public. I have rigidly excluded from these pages everything of a doubtful character, with the object in view of introducing my work into the schools for the instruction of the youth of my country.

The name of the famous body-servant of General Washington was George. After serving his illustrious master faithfully for half a century, and enjoying throughout this long term his high regard and confidence, it became his sorrowful duty at last to lay that beloved master to rest in his peaceful grave by the Potomac. Ten years afterward – in 1809 – full of years and honors, he died himself, mourned by all who knew him. The Boston *Gazette* of that date thus refers to the event:

George, the favorite body-servant of the lamented Washington, died in Richmond, Va., last Tuesday, at the ripe age of 95 years. His intellect was unimpaired, and his memory tenacious, up to within a few minutes of his decease. He was present at the second installation of Washington as President, and also at his funeral, and distinctly remembered all the prominent incidents connected with those noted events.

From this period we hear no more of the favorite body-servant of General Washington until May 1825, at which time he died again. A Philadelphia paper thus speaks of the sad occurrence:

At Macon, Ga., last week, a colored man named George, who was the favorite body-servant of General Washington, died at the advanced age of 95 years. Up to within a few hours of his dissolution he was in full possession of all his faculties, and could distinctly recollect the second installation of Washington, his death and burial, the surrender of Cornwallis, the battle of Trenton, the griefs and hardships of Valley Forge, etc. Deceased was followed to the grave by the entire population of Macon.

On the Fourth of July 1830, and also of 1834 and 1836, the subject of this sketch was exhibited in great state upon the rostrum of the orator of the day, and in November of 1840 he died again. The St Louis *Republican* of the 25th of that month spoke as follows:

ANOTHER RELIC OF THE REVOLUTION GONE

George, once the favorite body-servant of General Washington, died yesterday at the house of Mr John Leavenworth in this city, at the venerable age of 95 years. He was in the full possession of his faculties up to the hour of his death, and distinctly recollected the first and second installations and death of President Washington, the surrender of Cornwallis, the battles of Trenton and Monmouth, the sufferings of the patriot army at Valley Forge, the proclamation of the Declaration of Independence, the speech of Patrick Henry in the Virginia House of Delegates, and many other oldtime reminiscences of stirring interest. Few white men die lamented as was this aged negro. The funeral was very largely attended.

During the next ten or eleven years the subject of this sketch appeared at intervals at Fourth-of-July celebrations in various parts of the country, and was exhibited upon the rostrum with flattering success. But in the fall of 1855 he died again. The California papers thus speak of the event:

ANOTHER OLD HERO GONE

Died, at Dutch Flat, on the 7th of March, George (once the confidential body-servant of General Washington), at the great age of 95 years. His memory, which did not fail him till the last, was a wonderful storehouse of interesting reminiscences. He could distinctly recollect the first and second installations and death of President Washington, the surrender of Cornwallis, the battles of Trenton and Monmouth, and Bunker Hill, the proclamation of the Declaration of Independence, and Braddock's defeat. George was greatly respected in Dutch Flat, and it is estimated that there were 10,000 people present at his funeral.

The last time the subject of this sketch died was in June, 1864; and until we learn the contrary, it is just to presume that he died permanently this time. The Michigan papers thus refer to the sorrowful event:

ANOTHER CHERISHED REMNANT
OF THE REVOLUTION GONE

George, a colored man, and once the favorite body-servant of General Washington, died in Detroit last week, at the patriarchal age of 95 years. To the moment of his death his intellect was unclouded, and he could distinctly remember the first and second installations and death of Washington, the surrender of Cornwallis, the battles of Trenton and Monmouth, and Bunker Hill, the proclamation of the Declaration of Independence, Braddock's defeat, the throwing over of the tea in Boston harbor, and the landing of the Pilgrims. He died greatly respected, and was followed to the grave by a vast concourse of people.

The faithful old servant is gone! We shall never see him more until he turns up again. He has closed his long and splendid career of dissolution, for the present, and sleeps peacefully, as only they sleep who have earned their rest. He was in all respects a remarkable man. He held his age better than any celebrity that has figured in history; and the longer he lived the stronger and longer his memory grew. If he lives to die again, he will distinctly recollect the discovery of America.

The above résumé of his biography I believe to be substantially correct, although it is possible that he may have died once or twice in obscure places where the event failed of newspaper notoriety. One fault I find in all notices of his death which I have quoted, and this ought to be corrected. In them he uniformly and impartially died at the age of 95. This could not have been. He might have done that once, or maybe twice, but he could not have continued it indefinitely. Allowing that when he first died, he died at the age of 95, he was 151 years old when he died last, in 1864. But his age did not keep pace with his recollections. When he died the last time, he distinctly remembered the landing of the Pilgrims, which took place in 1620. He must have been about twenty years old when he witnessed that event, wherefore it is safe to assert that the body-servant of General Washington was in the neighborhood of two hundred and sixty or seventy years old when he departed this life finally.

Having waited a proper length of time, to see if the subject of this sketch had gone from us reliably and irrevocably, I now publish his biography with confidence, and respectfully offer it to a mourning nation.

PS – I see by the papers that this infamous old fraud has just died again, in Arkansas. This makes six times that he is known to have died, and always in a new place. The death of Washington's body-servant has ceased to be a novelty; its charm is gone; the people are tired of it; let it cease. This well-meaning but misguided negro has now put six different communities to the expense of burying him in state, and has swindled tens of thousands of people into following him to the grave under the delusion that a select and peculiar distinction was being conferred upon them. Let him stay buried for good now; and let that newspaper suffer the severest censure that shall ever, in all future time, publish to the world that General Washington's favorite colored body-servant has died again.

Burlesque Autobiography

Two or three persons having at different times intimated that if I would write an autobiography they would read it when they got leisure, I yield at last to this frenzied public demand, and herewith tender my history.

Ours is a noble old house, and stretches a long way back into antiquity. The earliest ancestor the Twains have any record of was a friend of the family by the name of Higgins. This was in the eleventh century, when our people were living in Aberdeen, county of Cork, England. Why it is that our long line has ever since borne the maternal name (except when one of them now and then took a playful refuge in an alias to avert foolishness) instead of Higgins, is a mystery which none of us has ever felt much desire to stir. It is a kind of vague pretty romance, and we leave it alone. All the old families do that way.

Arthour Twain was a man of considerable note – a solicitor on the highway in William Rufus's time. At about the age of thirty he went to one of those fine old English places of resort called Newgate, to see about something, and never returned again. While there he died suddenly.

Augustus Twain seems to have made something of a stir about the year 1160. He was as full of fun as he could be, and used to take his old sabre and sharpen it up, and get in a convenient place on a dark night, and stick it through people as they went by, to see them jump. He was a born humorist. But he got to going too far with it; and the first time he was found stripping one of these parties the authorities removed one end of him, and put it up on a nice high place on Temple Bar, where it could contemplate the people and have a good time. He never liked any situation so much or stuck to it so long.

Then for the next two hundred years the family tree shows a succession of soldiers – noble, high-spirited fellows, who always went into battle singing, right behind the army, and always went out a-whooping, right ahead of it.

This is a scathing rebuke to old dead Froissart's poor witticism, that our family tree never had but one limb to it, and that

that one stuck out at right angles, and bore fruit winter and summer.

Early in the fifteenth century we have Beau Twain, called 'the Scholar'. He wrote a beautiful, beautiful hand. And he could imitate anybody's hand so closely that it was enough to make a person laugh his head off to see it. He had infinite sport with his talent. But by and by he took a contract to break stone for a road, and the roughness of the work spoiled his hand. Still, he enjoyed life all the time he was in the stone business, which, with inconsiderable intervals, was some forty-two years. In fact, he died in harness. During all those long years he gave such satisfaction that he never was through with one contract a week till government gave him another. He was a perfect pet. And he was always a favorite with his fellow-artists, and was a conspicuous member of their benevolent secret society, called the Chain Gang. He always wore his hair short, had a preference for striped clothes, and died lamented by the government. He was a sore loss to his country, for he was so regular.

Some years later we have the illustrious John Morgan Twain. He came over to this country with Columbus in 1492 as a passenger. He appears to have been of a crusty, uncomfortable disposition. He complained of the food all the way over, and was always threatening to go ashore unless there was a change. He wanted fresh shad. Hardly a day passed over his head that he did not go idling about the ship with his nose in the air, sneering about the commander, and saying he did not believe Columbus knew where he was going to or had ever been there before. The memorable cry of 'Land ho!' thrilled every heart in the ship but his. He gazed a while through a piece of smoked glass at the pencilled line lying on the distant water, and then said, 'Land be hanged! It's a raft!'

When this questionable passenger came on board the ship he brought nothing with him but an old newspaper containing a handkerchief marked 'B. G.', one cotton sock marked 'L. W. C.', one woollen one marked 'D. F.', and a night-shirt marked 'O. M. R.' And yet during the voyage he worried more about his 'trunk', and gave himself more airs about it than all the rest of the passengers put together. If the ship was 'down by the head', and would not steer, he would go and move his 'trunk' further aft, and then watch the effect. If the ship was 'by the stern', he would suggest to Columbus to detail some men to 'shift that baggage'. In storms he had to be gagged, because his wailings about his 'trunk' made it impossible for the men to hear the orders. The man does not appear to have been openly charged with any gravely unbecoming thing, but it is noted in the ship's log as a 'curious circumstance' that, albeit he brought his baggage on board the ship in a newspaper, he took it ashore in four trunks, a queensware crate, and a couple of champagne baskets. But when he came back insinuating, in an insolent swaggering way, that some of his things were missing, and was going to search the other passengers' baggage, it was too much, and they threw him overboard. They watched long and wonderingly for him to come up, but not even a bubble rose on the quietly ebbing tide. But, while everyone was most absorbed in gazing over the side and the interest was momentarily increasing, it was observed with consternation that the vessel was adrift and the anchor cable hanging limp from the bow. Then in the ship's dimmed and ancient log we find this quaint note:

In time it was discovered y^t ye troublesome passenger hadde gonne downe and got ye anchor, and toke ye same and solde it to ye dam sauvages from ye interior, saying y^t he hadde *founde* y^t, ye sonne of a ghun!

Yet this ancestor had good and noble instincts, and it is with pride that we call to mind the fact that he was the first white person who ever interested himself in the work of elevating and civilizing our Indians. He built a commodious jail, and put up a gallows, and to his dying day he claimed with satisfaction that he had had a more restraining and elevating influence on the Indians than any other reformer that ever labored among them. At this point the chronicle became less frank and chatty, and closes abruptly by saying that the old voyager went to see his gallows perform on the first white man ever hanged in America, and while there received injuries which terminated in his death.

The great-grandson of the 'Reformer' flourished in sixteen hundred and something, and was known in our annals as 'the old Admiral', though in history he had other titles. He was long

in command of fleets of swift vessels, well armed and manned, and did great service in hurrying up merchantmen. Vessels which he followed and kept his eagle eye on always made good fair time across the ocean. But if a ship still loitered in spite of all he could do his indignation would grow till he could contain himself no longer – and then he would take that ship home where he lived and keep it there carefully, expecting the owners to come for it, but they never did. And he would try to get the idleness and sloth out of the sailors of that ship by compelling them to take invigorating exercise and a bath. He called it 'walking a plank'. All the pupils liked it. At any rate they never found any fault with it after trying it. When the owners were late coming for their ships, the Admiral always burned them, so that the insurance money should not be lost. At last this fine old tar was cut down in the fulness of his years and honors. And to her dying day his poor heart-broken widow believed that if he had been cut down fifteen minutes sooner he might have been resuscitated.

Charles Henry Twain lived during the latter part of the seventeenth century, and was a zealous and distinguished missionary. He converted sixteen thousand South Sea Islanders, and taught them that a dog-tooth necklace and a pair of spectacles was not enough clothing to come to divine service in. His poor flock loved him very, very dearly; and when his funeral was over they got up in a body (and came out of the restaurant) with tears in their eyes, and saying one to another that he was a good, tender missionary, and they wished they had some more of him.

Pah-go-to-wah-wah-pukketekeewis (Mighty-Hunter-with-a-Hog-Eye) Twain adorned the middle of the eighteenth century, and aided Gen. Braddock with all his heart to resist the oppressor Washington. It was this ancestor who fired seventeen times at our Washington from behind a tree. So far the beautiful romantic narrative in the moral story-books is correct, but when that narrative goes on to say that at the seventeenth round the awe-stricken savage said solemnly that that man was being reserved by the Great Spirit for some mighty mission, and he dared not lift his sacrilegious rifle against him again, the narrative seriously impairs the integrity of history. What he *did* say was –

'It ain't no (hic) no use. 'At man's so drunk he can't stan' still long enough for a man to hit him. I (hic!) *I* can't 'ford to fool away any more am'nition on *him!*'

That was why he stopped at the seventeenth round, and it was a good, plain, matter-of-fact reason, too, and one that easily commends itself to us by the eloquent persuasive flavor of probability there is about it.

I always enjoyed the story-book narrative, but I felt a marring misgiving that every Indian at Braddock's Defeat who fired at a soldier a couple of times (*two* easily grows to seventeen in a century), and missed him, jumped to the conclusion that the Great Spirit was reserving that soldier for some grand mission; and so I somehow feared that the only reason why Washington's case is remembered and the others forgotten is, that in his the prophecy came true, and in that of the others it didn't. There are not books enough on earth to contain the record of the prophecies Indians and other unauthorized parties have *made*; but one may carry in his overcoat pockets the record of all the prophecies that have been *fulfilled*.

I will remark here, in passing, that certain ancestors of mine are so thoroughly well known in history by their aliases that I have not felt it to be worth while to dwell upon them, or even mention them in the order of their birth. Among these may be mentioned Richard Brinsley Twain, alias Guy Fawkes; John Wentworth Twain, alias Sixteen-String Jack; William Hogarth Twain, alias Jack Sheppard; Ananias Twain, alias Baron Munchausen; John George Twain, alias Capt. Kydd. And then there are George Francis Train, Tom Pepper, Nebuchadnezzar, and Balaam's Ass: they all belong to our family, but to a branch of it somewhat distantly removed from the honorable direct line – in fact a collateral branch, whose members chiefly differ from the ancient stock in that, in order to acquire the notoriety we have always yearned and hungered for, they have got into a low way of going to jail instead of getting hanged.

It is not well, when writing an autobiography, to follow your ancestry down too close to your own time – it is safest to speak only vaguely of your great-grandfather, and then skip from there to yourself, which I now do.

I was born without teeth – and there Richard III had the

advantage of me; but I was born without a humpback likewise, and there I had the advantage of *him*. My parents were neither very poor nor conspicuously honest.

But now a thought occurs to me. My own history would really seem so tame contrasted with that of my ancestors that it is simply wisdom to leave it unwritten until I am hanged. If some other biographies I have read had stopped with the ancestry until a like event occurred it would have been a felicitous thing for the reading public. How does it strike *you*?

Running for Governor

A few months ago I was nominated for Governor of the great state of New York, to run against Mr John T. Smith and Mr Blank J. Blank on an independent ticket. I somehow felt that I had one prominent advantage over these gentlemen, and that was – good character. It was easy to see by the newspapers that if ever they had known what it was to bear a good name, that time had gone by. It was plain that in these latter years they had become familiar with all manner of shameful crimes. But at the very moment that I was exalting my advantage and joying in it in secret, there was a muddy undercurrent of discomfort 'riling' the deeps of my happiness, and that was – the having to hear my name bandied about in familiar connection with those of such people. I grew more and more disturbed. Finally I wrote my grandmother about it. Her answer came quick and sharp. She said: 'You have never done one single thing in all your life to be ashamed of – not one. Look at the newspapers – look at them and comprehend what sort of characters Messrs Smith and Blank are, and then see if you are willing to lower yourself to their level and enter a public canvass with them.'

It was my very thought! I did not sleep a single moment that night. But, after all, I could not recede. I was fully committed, and must go on with the fight. As I was looking listlessly over the papers at breakfast I came across this paragraph, and I may truly say I never was so confounded before.

PERJURY

Perhaps, now that Mr Mark Twain is before the people as a candidate for Governor, he will condescend to explain how he came to be convicted of perjury by thirty-four witnesses in Wakawak, Cochin China, in 1863, the intent of which perjury being to rob a poor native widow and her helpless family of a meager plantain-patch, their only stay and support in their bereavement and desolation. Mr Twain owes it to himself, as well as to the great people whose suffrages he asks, to clear this matter up. Will he do it?

I thought I should burst with amazement! Such a cruel, heart-less charge! I never had *seen* Cochin China! I never had *heard* of Wakawak! I didn't know a plantain-patch from a kangaroo! I did not know what to do. I was crazed and helpless. I let the day slip away without doing anything at all. The next morning the same paper had this – nothing more:

SIGNIFICANT

Mr Twain, it will be observed, is suggestively silent about the Cochin China perjury.

[*Mem*. During the rest of the campaign this paper never referred to me in any other way than as 'the infamous perjurer Twain'.]

Next came the *Gazette*, with this:

WANTED TO KNOW

Will the new candidate for Governor deign to explain to certain of his fellow-citizens (who are suffering to vote for him!) the little circumstance of his cabin-mates in Montana losing small valuables from time to time, until at last, these things having been invariably found on Mr Twain's person or in his 'Trunk' (newspaper he rolled his traps in), they felt compelled to give him a friendly admonition for his own good, and so tarred and feathered him, and rode him on a rail, and then advised him to leave a permanent vacuum in the place he usually occupied in the camp. Will he do this?

Could anything be more deliberately malicious than that? For I never was in Montana in my life. [After this, this journal customarily spoke of me as 'Twain, the Montana Thief'.]

I got to picking up papers apprehensively – much as one would lift a desired blanket which he had some idea might have a rattlesnake under it. One day this met my eye:

THE LIE NAILED

By the sworn affidavits of Michael O'Flanagan, Esq., of the Five Points, and Mr Snub Rafferty and Mr Catty Mulligan, of Water Street, it is established that Mr Mark Twain's vile statement that the lamented grandfather of our noble standard-bearer, Blank J. Blank, was hanged for highway robbery, is a brutal and gratuitous lie, without a shadow of foundation in fact. It is disheartening to virtuous men to see such shameful means resorted to to achieve political success as the attacking of the dead in their graves, and defiling their honored names with slander. When we think of the anguish this miserable falsehood must cause the innocent relatives and friends of the deceased, we are almost driven to incite an outraged and insulted public to summary and unlawful vengeance upon the traducer. But no! let us leave him to the agony of a lacerated conscience (though if passion should get the better of the public, and in its blind fury they should do the traducer bodily injury, it is but too obvious that no jury could convict and no court punish the perpetrators of the deed).

The ingenious closing sentence had the effect of moving me out of bed with despatch that night, and out at the back door also, while the 'outraged and insulted public' surged in the front way, breaking furniture and windows in their righteous indignation as they came, and taking off such property as they could carry when they went. And yet I can lay my hand upon the Book and say that I never slandered Mr Blank's grandfather. More: I had never even heard of him or mentioned him up to that day and date. [I will state, in passing, that the journal above quoted from always referred to me afterward as 'Twain, the Body-Snatcher'.]

The next newspaper article that attracted my attention was the following:

A SWEET CANDIDATE

Mr Mark Twain, who was to make such a blighting speech at the mass-meeting of the Independents last night, didn't come to time! A telegram from his physician stated that he had been knocked down by a runaway team, and his leg broken in two places – sufferer lying in great agony, and so forth, and so forth, and a lot more bosh of the same sort. And the Independents tried hard to swallow the wretched subterfuge, and pretend that they did not know what was the *real* reason of the absence of the abandoned creature whom they denominate their standard-bearer. *A certain man was seen to reel into Mr Twain's hotel last night in a state of beastly intoxication.* It is the imperative duty of the Independents to prove that this besotted brute was not Mark Twain himself. We have them at last! This is a case that admits of no shirking. The voice of the people demands in thunder tones, 'WHO WAS THAT MAN?'

It was incredible, absolutely incredible, for a moment, that it was really my name that was coupled with this disgraceful suspicion. Three long years had passed over my head since I had tasted ale, beer, wine, or liquor of any kind. [It shows what effect the times were having on me when I say that I saw myself confidently dubbed 'Mr Delirium Tremens Twain' in the next issue of that journal without a pang – notwithstanding I knew that with monotonous fidelity the paper would go on calling me so to the very end.]

By this time anonymous letters were getting to be an important part of my mail matter. This form was common:

How about that old woman you kiked of your premises which was beging.

POL. PRY

And this:

There is things which you have done which is unbeknowens to anybody but me. You better trot out a few dols, to yours truly, or you'll hear through the papers from

HANDY ANDY

This is about the idea. I could continue them till the reader was surfeited, if desirable.

Shortly the principal Republican journal 'convicted' me of wholesale bribery, and the leading Democratic paper 'nailed' an aggravated case of blackmailing to me. [In this way I acquired two additional names: 'Twain the Filthy Corruptionist' and 'Twain the Loathsome Embracer'.]

By this time there had grown to be such a clamor for an

137

'answer' to all the dreadful charges that were laid to me that the editors and leaders of my party said it would be political ruin for me to remain silent any longer. As if to make their appeal the more imperative, the following appeared in one of the papers the very next day:

BEHOLD THE MAN

The independent candidate still maintains silence. Because he dare not speak. Every accusation against him has been amply proved, and they have been endorsed and re-endorsed by his own eloquent silence, till at this day he stands forever convicted. Look upon your candidate, Independents! Look upon the Infamous Perjurer! the Montana Thief! the Body-Snatcher! Contemplate your incarnate Delirium Tremens! your Filthy Corruptionist! your Loathsome Embracer! Gaze upon him – ponder him well – and then say if you can give your honest votes to a creature who has earned this dismal array of titles by his hideous crimes, and dares not open his mouth in denial of any one of them!

There was no possible way of getting out of it, and so, in deep humiliation, I set about preparing to 'answer' a mass of baseless charges and mean and wicked falsehoods. But I never finished the task, for the very next morning a paper came out with a new horror, a fresh malignity, and seriously charged me with burning a lunatic asylum with all its inmates, because it obstructed the view from my house. This threw me into a sort of panic. Then came the charge of poisoning my uncle to get his property, with an imperative demand that the grave should be opened. This drove me to the verge of distraction. On top of this I was accused of employing toothless and incompetent old relatives to prepare the food for the foundling hospital when I was warden. I was wavering – wavering. And at last, as a due and fitting climax to the shameless persecution that party rancor had inflicted upon me, nine little toddling children, of all shades of color and degrees of raggedness, were taught to rush onto the platform at a public meeting, and clasp me around the legs and call me PA!

I gave it up. I hauled down my colors and surrendered. I was not equal to the requirements of a Gubernatorial campaign in the state of New York, and so I sent in my withdrawal from the candidacy, and in bitterness of spirit signed it, 'Truly yours, *once* a decent man, but now MARK TWAIN, IP, MT, BS, DT, FC, and LE'.

The Case of George Fisher

This is history. It is not a wild extravaganza, like 'John Wilson Mackenzie's Great Beef Contract', but is a plain statement of facts and circumstances with which the Congress of the United States has interested itself from time to time during the long period of half a century.

I will not call this matter of George Fisher's a great deathless and unrelenting swindle upon the government and people of the United States – for it has never been so decided, and I hold that it is a grave and solemn wrong for a writer to cast slurs or call names when such is the case – but will simply present the evidence and let the reader deduce his own verdict. Then we shall do nobody injustice, and our consciences shall be clear.

On or about the 1st day of September, 1813, the Creek war being then in progress in Florida, the crops, herds, and houses of Mr George Fisher, a citizen, were destroyed, either by the Indians or by the United States troops in pursuit of them. By the terms of the law, if the *Indians* destroyed the property, there was no relief for Fisher; but if the *troops* destroyed it, the Government of the United States was debtor to Fisher for the amount involved.

George Fisher must have considered that the *Indians* destroyed the property, because, although he lived several years afterward, he does not appear to have ever made any claim upon the Government.

In the course of time Fisher died, and his widow married again. And by and by, nearly twenty years after that dimly remembered raid upon Fisher's cornfields, *the widow Fisher's new husband* petitioned Congress to pay for the property, and backed up the petition with many depositions and affidavits which purported to prove that the troops, and not the Indians, destroyed the property; that the troops, for some inscrutable reason, deliberately burned down 'houses' (or cabins) valued at $600, the same belonging to a peaceable private citizen, and also destroyed various other property belonging to the same citizen. But Congress declined to believe that the troops were such idiots (after overtaking and scattering a band of Indians proved to have been found destroying Fisher's property) as to calmly continue the work of destruction themselves, and make a complete job of what the Indians had only commenced. So Congress denied the petition of the heirs of George Fisher in 1832, and did not pay them a cent.

We hear no more from them officially until 1848, sixteen years after their first attempt on the Treasury, and a full generation after the death of the man whose fields were destroyed. The new generation of Fisher heirs then came forward and put in a bill for damages. The Second Auditor awarded them $8,873, being half the damage sustained by Fisher. The Auditor said the testimony showed that at least half the destruction was done by the Indians *'before the troops started in pursuit'*, and of course the government was not responsible for that half.

2. That was in April 1848. In December 1848, the heirs of George Fisher, deceased, came forward and pleaded for a 'revision' of their bill of damages. The revision was made, but nothing new could be found in their favor except an error of $100 in the former calculation. However, in order to keep up the spirits of the Fisher family, the Auditor concluded to go back and allow *interest* from the date of the first petition (1832) to the date when the bill of damages was awarded. This sent the Fishers home happy with sixteen years' interest on $8,873 – the same amounting to $8,997.94. Total, $17,870.94.

3. For an entire year the suffering Fisher family remained quiet – even satisfied, after a fashion. Then they swooped down upon the Government with their wrongs once more. That old patriot, Attorney-General Toucey, burrowed through the musty papers of the Fishers and discovered one more chance for the desolate orphans – interest on that original award of $8,873 from date of destruction of the property (1813) up to 1832! Result, $10,004.89 for the indigent Fishers. So now we have: First, $8,873 damages; second, interest on it from 1832 to 1848, $8,997.94; third, interest on it dated back to 1813, $10,004.89. Total, $27,875.83! What better investment for a great-grand-child than to get the Indians to burn a cornfield for him sixty or seventy years before his birth, and plausibly lay it on lunatic United States troops?

4. Strange as it may seem, the Fishers let Congress alone for five years – or, what is perhaps more likely, failed to make themselves heard by Congress for that length of time. But at last, in 1854, they got a hearing. They persuaded Congress to pass an act requiring the Auditor to re-examine their case. But this time they stumbled upon the misfortune of an honest Secretary of the Treasury (Mr James Guthrie), and he spoiled everything. He said in very plain language that the Fishers were not only not entitled to another cent, but that those children of many sorrows and acquainted with grief *had been paid too much already*.

5. Therefore another interval of rest and silence ensued – an interval which lasted four years – viz., till 1858. The 'right man in the right place' was then Secretary of War – John B. Floyd, of peculiar renown! Here was a master intellect; here was the very man to succor the suffering heirs of dead and forgotten Fisher. They came up from Florida with a rush – a great tidal wave of Fishers freighted with the same old musty documents about the same immortal cornfields of their ancestor. They straightway got an act passed transferring the Fisher matter from the dull Auditor to the ingenious Floyd. What did Floyd do? He said, 'IT WAS PROVED *that the Indians destroyed everything they could before the troops entered in pursuit.*' He considered, therefore, that what they destroyed must have consisted of '*the houses with all their contents, and the liquor*' (the most trifling part of the destruction, and set down at only $3,200 all told), and that the government troops then drove them off and calmly proceeded to destroy –

Two hundred and twenty acres of corn in the field, thirty-five acres of wheat, and nine hundred and eighty-six head of livestock! [What a singularly intelligent army we had in those days, according to Mr Floyd – though not according to the Congress of 1832.]

So Mr Floyd decided that the Government was not responsible for that $3,200 worth of rubbish which the Indians destroyed, but was responsible for the property destroyed by the troops – which property consisted of (I quote from the printed United States Senate document):

	DOLLARS
Corn at Bassett's Creek	3,000
Cattle	5,000
Stock hogs	1,050
Drove hogs	1,204
Wheat	350
Hides	4,000
Corn on the Alabama River	3,500
Total	18,104

That sum, in his report, Mr Floyd calls the '*full value* of the property destroyed by the troops'. He allows that sum to the starving Fishers, TOGETHER WITH INTEREST FROM 1813. From this new sum total the amounts already paid to the Fishers were deducted, and then the cheerful remainder (a fraction under *forty thousand dollars*) was handed to them, and again they retired to Florida in a condition of temporary tranquility. Their ancestor's farm had now yielded them altogether nearly *sixty-seven thousand dollars* in cash.

6. Does the reader suppose that that was the end of it? Does he suppose those diffident Fishers were satisfied? Let the evidence show. The Fishers were quiet just two years. Then they came swarming up out of the fertile swamps of Florida with their same old documents and besieged Congress once more. Congress capitulated on the 1st of June, 1860, and instructed Mr Floyd to overhaul those papers again and pay that bill. A Treasury clerk was ordered to go through those papers and report to Mr Floyd what amount was still due the emaciated Fishers. This clerk (I can produce him whenever he is wanted) discovered what was apparently a glaring and recent forgery in the papers, whereby a witness's testimony as to the price of corn in Florida in 1813 was made to name double the amount which that witness had originally specified as the price! The clerk not only called his superior's attention to this thing, but in making up his brief of the case called particular attention to it in writing. That part of the brief *never got before Congress*, nor has Congress ever yet had a hint of a forgery existing among the Fisher papers. Nevertheless, on the basis of the double prices (and totally ignoring the clerk's assertion that the figures were manifestly

and unquestionably a recent forgery), Mr Floyd remarks in his new report that 'the testimony, *particularly in regard to the corn crops*, DEMANDS A MUCH HIGHER ALLOWANCE than any *heretofore* made by the Auditor or myself.' So he estimates the crop at *sixty bushels* to the acre (double what Florida acres pro- duce), and then virtuously allows pay for only half the crop *but* allows *two dollars and a half* a bushel for that half, when there are rusty old books and documents in the Congressional library to show just what the Fisher testimony showed before the forgery – viz., that in the fall of 1813 corn was only worth from $1.25 to $1.50 a bushel. Having accomplished this, what does Mr Floyd do next? Mr Floyd ('with an earnest desire to execute truly the legislative will', as he piously remarks) goes to work and makes out an entirely new bill of Fisher damages, and in this new bill he placidly *ignores the Indians* altogether – puts no particle of the destruction of the Fisher property upon them, but, even repent- ing him of charging them with burning the cabins and drinking the whiskey and breaking the crockery, lays the *entire* damage at the door of the imbecile United States troops down to the very last item! And not only that, but uses the forgery to double the loss of corn at 'Bassett's Creek', and uses it again to absolutely *treble* the loss of corn on the 'Alabama River'. This new and ably conceived and executed bill of Mr Floyd's figures up as follows (I copy again from the printed United States Senate document):

THE UNITED STATES IN ACCOUNT WITH THE LEGAL
REPRESENTATIVES OF GEORGE FISHER, DECEASED

		DOL. C.
1813	To 550 head of cattle, at 10 dollars	5,500.00
	To 86 head of drove hogs	1,204.00
	To 350 head of stock hogs	1,750.00
	To 100 ACRES OF CORN ON BASSETT'S CREEK	6,000.00
	To *8 barrels of whiskey*	350.00
	To *2 barrels of brandy*	280.00
	To *1 barrel of rum*	70.00
	To *dry-goods and merchandise in store*	1,100.00
	To 35 acres of wheat	350.00
	To 2,000 hides	4,000.00

	To furs and hats in store	600.00
	To crockery ware in store	100.00
	To smith's and carpenter's tools	250.00
	To houses burned and destroyed	600.00
	To 4 dozen bottles of wine	48.00
1814	To 120 acres of corn on Alabama River	9,500.00
	To crops of peas, fodder, etc.	3,250.00
	Total	34,952.00

To interest on $22,202, from July 1813 to November 1860, 47 years and 4 months	63,053.68
To interest on $12,750, from September 1814 to November 1860, 46 years and 2 months	35,317.50
Total	133,323.18

He puts everything in this time. He does not even allow that the Indians destroyed the crockery or drank the four dozen bottles of (currant) wine. When it came to supernatural comprehensiveness in 'gobbling', John B. Floyd was without his equal, in his own or any other generation. Subtracting from the above total the $67,000 already paid to George Fisher's implacable heirs, Mr Floyd announced that the Government was still indebted to them in the sum of *sixty-six thousand five hundred and nineteen dollars and eighty-five cents*, 'which' Mr Floyd complacently remarks, 'will be paid, accordingly, to the administrator of the estate of George Fisher, deceased, or to his attorney in fact.'

But, sadly enough for the destitute orphans, a new President came in just at this time, Buchanan and Floyd went out, and they never got their money. The first thing Congress did in 1861 was to rescind the resolution of June 1, 1860, under which Mr Floyd had been ciphering. Then Floyd (and doubtless the heirs of George Fisher likewise) had to give up financial business for a while, and go into the Confederate army and serve their country.

Were the heirs of George Fisher killed? No. They are back now at this very time (July 1870), beseeching Congress through that blushing and diffident creature, Garrett Davis, to commence making payments again on their interminable and insatiable bill of damages for corn and whiskey destroyed by a gang of irresponsible Indians, so long ago that even government red-tape has failed to keep consistent and intelligent track of it.

Now the above are facts. They are history. Anyone who doubts it can send to the Senate Document Department of the Capitol for H. R. Ex. Doc. No. 21, 36th Congress, 2nd Session, and for S. Ex. Doc. No. 106, 41st Congress, 2nd Session, and satisfy himself. The whole case is set forth in the first volume of the Court of Claims Reports.

It is my belief that as long as the continent of America holds together, the heirs of George Fisher, deceased, will still make pilgrimages to Washington from the swamps of Florida, to plead for just a little more cash on their bill of damages (even when they received the last of that sixty-seven thousand dollars, they said it was only *one-fourth* what the Government owed them on that fruitful cornfield), and as long as they choose to come they will find Garrett Davises to drag their vampire schemes before Congress. This is not the only hereditary fraud (if fraud it is – which I have before repeatedly remarked is not proven) that is being quietly handed down from generation to generation of fathers and sons, through the persecuted Treasury of the United States.

Curing a Cold

It is a good thing, perhaps, to write for the amusement of the public, but it is a far higher and nobler thing to write for their instruction, their profit, their actual and tangible benefit. The latter is the sole object of this article. If it prove the means of restoring to health one solitary sufferer among my race, of lighting up once more the fire of hope and joy in his faded eyes, of bringing back to his dead heart again the quick, generous impulses of other days, I shall be amply rewarded for my labor; my soul will be permeated with the sacred delight a Christian feels when he has done a good, unselfish deed.

Having led a pure and blameless life, I am justified in believing that no man who knows me will reject the suggestions I am about to make, out of fear that I am trying to deceive him. Let the public do itself the honor to read my experience in doctoring a cold, as herein set forth, and then follow in my footsteps.

When the White House was burned in Virginia, I lost my home, my happiness, my constitution, and my trunk. The loss of the two first-named articles was a matter of no great consequence, since a home without a mother or a sister, or a distant young female relative in it, to remind you, by putting your soiled linen out of sight and taking your boots down off the mantelpiece, that there are those who think about you and care for you, is easily obtained. And I cared nothing for the loss of my happiness, because, not being a poet, it could not be possible that melancholy would abide with me long.

But to lose a good constitution and a better trunk were serious misfortunes.

On the day of the fire my constitution succumbed to a severe cold caused by undue exertion in getting ready to do something. I suffered to no purpose, too, because the plan I was figuring at for the extinguishing of the fire was so elaborate that I never got it completed until the middle of the following week.

The first time I began to sneeze, a friend told me to go and bathe my feet in hot water and go to bed. I did so. Shortly afterwards, another friend advised me to get up and take a cold shower-bath. I did that also. Within the hour, another friend assured me that it was policy to 'feed a cold and starve a fever'. I had both. So I thought it best to fill myself up for the cold, and then keep dark and let the fever starve awhile.

In a case of this kind, I seldom do things by halves; I ate pretty heartily; I conferred my custom upon a stranger who had just opened his restaurant that morning; he waited near me in respectful silence until I had finished feeding my cold, when he inquired if the people about Virginia were much afflicted with colds? I told him I thought they were.

He then went out and took in his sign.

I started down toward the office, and on the way encountered another bosom friend, who told me that a quart of salt water, taken warm, would come as near curing a cold as anything in the world. I hardly thought I had room for it, but I tried it anyhow. The result was surprising. I believe I threw up my immortal soul.

Now, as I am giving my experience only for the benefit of those who are troubled with the distemper I am writing about, I feel that they will see the propriety of my cautioning them against following such portions of it as proved inefficient with me, and, acting upon this conviction, I warn them against warm salt water. It may be a good enough remedy, but I think it is too severe. If I had another cold in the head, and there was no course left me but to take either an earthquake or a quart of warm salt water, I would take my chances on the earthquake.

After the storm which had been raging in my stomach had subsided, and no more good Samaritans happening along, I went on borrowing handkerchiefs again and blowing them to atoms, as had been my custom in the early stages of my cold, until I came across a lady who had just arrived from over the plains, and who said she had lived in a part of the country where doctors were scarce, and had from necessity acquired considerable skill in the treatment of simple 'family complaints'. I knew she must have had much experience, for she appeared to be a hundred and fifty years old.

She mixed a decoction composed of molasses, aquafortis, turpentine, and various other drugs, and instructed me to take a wineglass full of it every fifteen minutes. I never took but one dose; that was enough; it robbed me of all moral principle, and awoke every unworthy impulse of my nature. Under its malign influence my brain conceived miracles of meanness, but my hands were too feeble to execute them; at that time, had it not been that my strength had surrendered to a succession of assaults from infallible remedies for my cold, I am satisfied that I would have tried to rob the graveyard.

Like most other people I often feel mean, and act accordingly; but until I took that medicine I had never reveled in such supernatural depravity and felt proud of it. At the end of two days I was ready to go to doctoring again. I took a few more unfailing remedies, and finally drove my cold from my head to my lungs.

I got to coughing incessantly, and my voice fell below zero; I conversed in a thundering bass, two octaves below my natural tone; I could only compass my regular nightly repose by coughing myself down to a state of utter exhaustion, and then the moment I began to talk in my sleep my discordant voice woke me up again.

My case grew more and more serious every day. Plain gin was recommended; I took it. Then gin and molasses; I took that also. Then gin and onions; I added the onions, and took all three. I detected no particular result.

I found I had to travel for my health. I went to Lake Tahoe with my reportorial comrade, Wilson. It is gratifying to me to reflect that we traveled in considerable style; we went in the Pioneer coach, and my friend took all his baggage with him, consisting of two excellent silk handkerchiefs and a daguerreotype of his grandmother. We sailed, and hunted, and fished, and danced all day, and I doctored my cough all night. By managing in this way, I made out to improve every hour in the twenty-four. But my disease continued to grow worse.

A sheet-bath was recommended. I had never refused a remedy yet, and it seemed poor policy to commence then; therefore I determined to take a sheet-bath, notwithstanding I had no idea what sort of arrangement it was.

It was administered at midnight, and the weather was very frosty. My breast and back were bared, and a sheet (there appeared to be a thousand yards of it) soaked in ice-water was wound around me until I resembled a swab for a Columbiad.

It is a cruel expedient. When the chilly rag touches one's warm flesh it makes him start with sudden violence and gasp for breath, just as men do in the death agony. It froze the marrow in my bones and stopped the beating of my heart. I thought my time had come.

Never take a sheet-bath – never. Next to meeting a lady acquaintance, who, for reasons best known to herself, don't see you when she looks at you, and don't know you when she does see you, it is the most uncomfortable thing in the world.

But, as I was saying, when the sheet-bath failed to cure my cough, a lady friend recommended the application of a mustard plaster to my breast. I believe that would have cured me effectually, if it had not been for young Wilson. When I went to bed I put my mustard plaster – which was a very gorgeous one, eighteen inches square – where I could reach it when I was ready for it. But young Wilson got hungry in the night, and—

After sojourning a week at Lake Tahoe, I went to Steamboat Springs, and beside the steam baths, I took a cargo of the wickedest medicines that were ever concocted. They would have cured me, but I had to go back to Virginia, where, notwithstanding the variety of new remedies I absorbed every day, I managed to aggravate my disease by carelessness and undue exposure.

I finally concluded to visit San Francisco, and the first day I got there, a lady at the Lick House told me to drink a quart of whiskey every twenty-four hours, and a friend at the Occidental recommended precisely the same course. Each advised me to take a quart; that made half a gallon. I did it, and still live.

Now, with the kindest motives in the world, I offer for the consideration of consumptive patients the variegated course of treatment I have lately gone through. Let them try it; if it don't cure, it can't more than kill them.

A Day's Work!

Saturday morning was come, and all the summer world was bright and fresh, and brimming with life. There was a song in every heart; and if the heart was young the music issued at the lips. There was cheer in every face and a spring in every step. The locust-trees were in bloom, and the fragrance of the blossoms filled the air. Cardiff Hill, beyond the village and above it, was green with vegetation, and it lay just far enough away to seem a Delectable Land, dreamy, reposeful, and inviting.

Tom appeared on the sidewalk with a bucket of whitewash and a long-handled brush. He surveyed the fence, and all gladness left him and a deep melancholy settled down upon his spirit. Thirty yards of board fence nine feet high! Life to him seemed hollow, and existence but a burden. Sighing, he dipped his brush and passed it along the topmost plank; repeated the operation; did it again; compared the insignificant whitewashed streak with the far-reaching continent of unwhitewashed fence, and sat down on a tree-box discouraged. Jim came skipping out at the gate with a tin pail, and singing 'Buffalo Gals'. Bringing water from the town pump had always been hateful work in Tom's eyes before, but now it did not strike him so. He remembered that there was company at the pump. White, mulatto, and negro boys and girls always were there waiting their turns, resting, trading playthings, quarreling, fighting, skylarking. And he remembered that, although the pump was only a hundred and fifty yards off, Jim never got back with a bucket of water under an hour – and even then somebody generally had to go after him. Tom said:

'Say, Jim, I'll fetch the water if you'll whitewash some.'

Jim shook his head and said:

'Can't, Mars Tom. Ole missis, she tole me I got to go an' git dis water an' not stop foolin' roun' wid anybody. She say she spec' Mars Tom gwine to ax me to whitewash, an' so she tole me go 'long an' 'tend to my own business – she 'lowed *she'd* 'tend to de whitewashin'.'

'Oh, never you mind what she said, Jim. That's the way she

talks. Gimme the bucket – I won't be gone only a minute. *She* won't ever know.'

'Oh, I dasn't, Mars Tom. Ole missis she'd take an' tar de head off'n me. 'Deed she would.'

'*She!* She never licks anybody – whacks 'em over the head with her thimble – and who cares for that, I'd like to know? She talks awful, but talk don't hurt – anyways, it don't if she don't cry. Jim, I'll give you a marvel. I'll give you a white alley!'

Jim began to waver.

'White alley, Jim! And it's a bully taw.'

'My! Dat's a mighty gay marvel, *I* tell you! But, Mars Tom, I's powerful 'fraid ole missis—'

'And besides, if you will I'll show you my sore toe.'

Jim was only human – this attraction was too much for him. He put down his pail, took the white alley, and bent over the toe with absorbing interest while the bandage was being unwound. In another moment he was flying down the street with his pail and a tingling rear, Tom was whitewashing with vigor, and Aunt Polly was retiring from the field with a slipper in her hand and triumph in her eye.

But Tom's energy did not last. He began to think of the fun he had planned for this day, and his sorrows multiplied. Soon the free boys would come tripping along on all sorts of delicious expeditions, and they would make a world of fun of him for having to work – the very thought of it burnt him like fire. He got out his worldly wealth and examined it – bits of toys, marbles, and trash; enough to buy an exchange of *work*, maybe, but not half enough to buy so much as half an hour of pure freedom. So he returned his straitened means to his pocket, and gave up the idea of trying to buy the boys. At this dark and hopeless moment an inspiration burst upon him! Nothing less than a great, magnificent inspiration.

He took up his brush and went tranquilly to work. Ben Rogers hove in sight presently – the very boy, of all boys, whose ridicule he had been dreading. Ben's gait was the hop-skip-and-jump – proof enough that his heart was light and his anticipations high. He was eating an apple, and giving a long, melodious whoop, at intervals, followed by a deep-toned ding-dong-dong, for he was personating a steamboat. As he drew near, he slackened speed, took the middle of the street, leaned far over to starboard, and rounded to ponderously and with laborious pomp and circumstance – for he was personating the *Big Missouri*, and considered himself to be drawing nine feet of water. He was boat and captain and engine-bells combined, so he had to imagine himself standing on his own hurricane-deck giving the orders and executing them:

'Stop her, sir! Ting-a-ling-ling!' The headway ran almost out, and he drew up slowly toward the sidewalk.

'Ship up to back! Ting-a-ling-ling!' His arms straightened and stiffened down his sides.

'Set her back on the stabbord! Ting-a-ling-ling! Chow! ch-chow-wow! Chow!' His right hand, meantime, describing stately circles – for it was representing a forty-foot wheel.

'Let her go back on the labbord! Ting-a-ling-ling! Chow-ch-chow-chow!' The left hand began to describe circles.

'Stop the stabbord! Ting-a-ling-ling! Stop the labbord! Come ahead on the stabbord! Stop her! Let your outside turn over slow! Ting-a-ling-ling! Chow-ow-ow! Get out that head-line! *Lively* now! Come – out with your spring-line – what're you about there! Take a turn round that stump with the bight of it! Stand by that stage, now – let her go! Done with the engines, sir! Ting-a-ling-ling! *Sh't! sh't! sh't!*' (trying the gauge-cocks).

Tom went on whitewashing – paid no attention to the steamboat. Ben stared a moment, and then said:

'Hi-*yi*! *You're* up a stump, ain't you?'

No answer. Tom surveyed his last touch with the eye of an artist; then he gave his brush another gentle sweep and surveyed the result, as before. Ben ranged up alongside of him. Tom's mouth watered for the apple, but he stuck to his work. Ben said:

'Hallo, old chap, you got to work, hey?'

Tom wheeled suddenly and said:

'Why, it's you, Ben! I warn't noticing.'

'Say – I'm going in a-swimming, *I* am. Don't you wish you could? But of course you'd druther *work* – wouldn't you? Course you would!'

Tom contemplated the boy a bit, and said:

'What do you call work?'

'Why, ain't *that* work?'

Tom resumed his whitewashing, and answered carelessly:

'Well, maybe it is, and maybe it ain't. All I know is, it suits Tom Sawyer.'

'Oh, come, now, you don't mean to let on that you *like* it?'

The brush continued to move.

'Like it? Well, I don't see why I oughtn't to like it. Does a boy get a chance to whitewash a fence every day?'

That put the thing in a new light. Ben stopped nibbling his apple. Tom swept his brush daintily back and forth – stepped back to note the effect – added a touch here and there – criticized the effect again – Ben watching every move and getting more and more interested, more and more absorbed. Presently he said:

'Say, Tom, let *me* whitewash a little.'

Tom considered, was about to consent; but he altered his mind.

'No – no – I reckon it wouldn't hardly do, Ben. You see Aunt Polly's awful particular about this fence – right here on the street, you know – but if it was the back fence I wouldn't mind, and *she* wouldn't. Yes, she's awful particular about this fence; it's got to be done very careful; I reckon there ain't one boy in a thousand, maybe two thousand, that can do it the way it's got to be done.'

'No – is that so? Oh, come, now – lemme just try. Only just a little – I'd let *you*, if you was me, Tom.'

'Ben, I'd like to, honest injun; but Aunt Polly – well, Jim wanted to do it, but she wouldn't let him. Sid wanted to do it, and she wouldn't let Sid. Now don't you see how I'm fixed? If you was to tackle this fence, and anything was to happen to it—'

'Oh, shucks, I'll be just as careful. Now, lemme try. Say – I'll give you the core of my apple.'

'Well, here—No, Ben, now don't. I'm afeared—'

'I'll give you *all* of it!'

Tom gave up the brush, with reluctance in his face but alacrity in his heart. And while the late steamer *Big Missouri* worked and sweated in the sun, the retired artist sat on a barrel in the shade close by, dangled his legs, munched his apple, and planned the slaughter of more innocents. There was no lack of material;

boys happened along every little while; they came to jeer, but remained to whitewash. By the time Ben was fagged out, Tom had traded the next chance to Billy Fisher for a kite, in good repair; and when *he* played out, Johnny Miller bought in for a dead rat and a string to swing it with – and so on, and so on, hour after hour. And when the middle of the afternoon came, from being a poor poverty-stricken boy in the morning, Tom was literally rolling in wealth. He had, beside the things before mentioned, twelve marbles, part of a jew's-harp, a piece of blue bottle-glass to look through, a spool cannon, a key that wouldn't unlock anything, a fragment of chalk, a glass stopper of a decanter, a tin soldier, a couple of tadpoles, six fire-crackers, a kitten with only one eye, a brass door-knob, a dog-collar – but no dog – the handle of a knife, four pieces of orange-peel, and a dilapidated old window-sash.

The Adventures of Tom Sawyer

The Undertaker's Chat

'Now that corpse', said the undertaker, patting the folded hands of deceased approvingly, 'was a brick – every way you took him he was a brick. He was so real accommodating, and so modest-like and simple in his last moments. Friends wanted metallic burial-case – nothing else would do. *I* couldn't get it. There warn't going to be time – anybody could see that.

'Corpse said never mind, shake him up some kind of a box he could stretch out in comfortable, *he* warn't particular 'bout the general style of it. Said he went more on room than style, any-way in a last final container.

'Friends wanted a silver door-plate on the coffin, signifying who he was and wher' he was from. Now *you* know a fellow couldn't roust out such a gaily thing as that in a little country-town like this. What did corpse say?

'Corpse said, whitewash his old canoe and dob his address and general destination onto it with a blacking-brush and a stencil-plate, 'long with a verse from some likely hymn or other, and p'int him for the tomb, and mark him COD, and just let him flicker. *He* warn't distressed any more than you be – on the contrary, just as ca'm and collected as a hearse-horse; said he judged that wher' he was going to a body would find it considerable better to attract attention by a picturesque moral character than a natty burial-case with a swell door-plate on it.

'Splendid man, he was. I'd druther do for a corpse like that 'n any I've tackled in seven year. There's some satisfaction in buryin' a man like that. You feel that what you're doing is appreciated. Lord bless you, so's he got planted before he sp'iled, he was perfectly satisfied; said his relations meant well, *perfectly* well, but all them preparations was bound to delay the thing more or less, and he didn't wish to be kept layin' around. You never see such a clear head as what he had – and so ca'm and so cool. Jist a hunk of brains – that is what *he* was. Perfectly awful. It was a ripping distance from one end of that man's head to t'other. Often and over again he's had brain-fever a-raging in

one place, and the rest of the pile didn't know anything about it – didn't affect it any more than an Injun insurrection in Arizona affects the Atlantic States.

'Well, the relations they wanted a big funeral, but corpse said he was down on flummery – didn't want any procession – fill the hearse full of mourners, and get out a stern line and tow *him* behind. He *was* the most down on style of any remains I ever struck. A beautiful, simple-minded creature – it was what he was, you can depend on that. He was just set on having things the way he wanted them, and he took a solid comfort in laying his little plans. He had me measure him and take a whole raft of directions; then he had the minister stand up behind a long box with a tablecloth over it, to represent the coffin, and read his funeral sermon, saying "Angcore, angcore!" at the good places, and making him scratch out every bit of brag about him, and all the hifalutin; and then he made them trot out the choir, so's he could help them pick out the tunes for the occasion, and he got them to sing "Pop Goes the Weasel", because he'd always liked that tune when he was downhearted, and solemn music made him sad; and when they sung that with tears in their eyes (because they all loved him), and his relations grieving around, he just laid there as happy as a bug, and trying to beat time and showing all over how much he enjoyed it; and presently he got worked up and excited, and tried to join in, for, mind you, he was pretty proud of his abilities in the singing line; but the first time he opened his mouth and was just going to spread himself his breath took a walk.

'I never see a man snuffed out so sudden. Ah, it was a great loss – a powerful loss to this poor little one-horse town. Well, well, well, I hain't got time to be palavering along here – got to nail on the lid and mosey along with him; and if you'll just give me a lift we'll skeet him into the hearse and meander along. Relations bound to have it so – don't pay no attention to dying injunctions, minute a corpse's gone; but, if I had *my* way, if I didn't respect his last wishes and tow him behind the hearse *I'll* be cuss'd. I consider that whatever a corpse wants done for his comfort is little enough matter, and a man hain't got no right to deceive him or take advantage of him; and whatever a corpse trusts me to do I'm a-going to *do*, you know, even if it's to stuff

157

him and paint him yaller and keep him for a keepsake – you hear *me!*'

He cracked his whip and went lumbering away with his ancient ruin of a hearse, and I continued my walk with a valuable lesson learned – that a healthy and wholesome cheerfulness is not necessarily impossible to *any* occupation. The lesson is likely to be lasting, for it will take many months to obliterate the memory of the remarks and circumstances that impressed it.

An American in Europe

For some days we were content to enjoy looking at the blue lake
Lucerne and at the piled-up masses of snow-mountains that border it all around – an enticing spectacle, this last, for there is a
strange and fascinating beauty and charm about a majestic
snow-peak with the sun blazing upon it or the moonlight softly
enriching it – but finally we concluded to try a bit of excursion-
ing around on a steamboat, and a dash on foot at the Rigi. Very
well, we had a delightful trip to Fluelen, on a breezy, sunny day.
Everybody sat on the upper deck, on benches, under an awning;
everybody talked, laughed, and exclaimed at the wonderful
scenery; in truth, a trip on that lake is almost the perfection of
pleasuring. The mountains were a never-ceasing marvel. Sometimes they rose straight up out of the lake, and towered aloft and
overshadowed our pygmy steamer with their prodigious bulk in
the most impressive way. Not snow-clad mountains, these, yet
they climbed high enough toward the sky to meet the clouds
and veil their foreheads in them. They were not barren and
repulsive, but clothed in green, and restful and pleasant to the
eye. And they were so almost straight-up-and-down, sometimes,
that one could not imagine a man being able to keep his footing
upon such a surface, yet there are paths, and the Swiss people go
up and down them every day.

Sometimes one of these monster precipices had the slight
inclination of the huge ship-houses in dockyards – then high
aloft, toward the sky, it took a little stronger inclination, like
that of a mansard roof – and perched on this dizzy mansard
one's eye detected little things like martin boxes, and presently
perceived that these were the dwellings of peasants – an airy
place for a home, truly. And suppose a peasant should walk in
his sleep, or his child should fall out of the front yard? – the
friends would have a tedious long journey down out of those
cloud-heights before they found the remains. And yet those
faraway homes looked ever so seductive, they were so remote
from the troubled world, they dozed in such an atmosphere of
peace and dreams – surely no one who had learned to live up

there would ever want to live on a meaner level.

We swept through the prettiest little curving arms of the lake, among these colossal green walls, enjoying new delights, always, as the stately panorama unfolded itself before us and rerolled and hid itself behind us; and now and then we had the thrilling surprise of bursting suddenly upon a tremendous white mass like the distant and dominating Jungfrau, or some kindred giant, looming head and shoulders above a tumbled waste of lesser Alps.

Once, while I was hungrily taking in one of these surprises, and doing my best to get all I possibly could of it while it should last, I was interrupted by a young and carefree voice:

'You're an American, I think – so'm I.'

He was about eighteen, or possibly nineteen; slender and of medium height; open, frank, happy face; a restless but independent eye; a snub nose, which had the air of drawing back with a decent reserve from the silky new-born mustache below it until it should be introduced; a loosely hung jaw, calculated to work easily in the sockets. He wore a low-crowned, narrow-brimmed straw hat, with a broad blue ribbon around it which had a white anchor embroidered on it in front; nobby short-tailed coat, pantaloons, vest, all trim and neat and up with the fashion; red-striped stockings, very low-quarter patent-leather shoes tied with black ribbon; blue ribbon around his neck, wide-open collar; tiny diamond studs; wrinkleless kids; projecting cuffs, fastened with large oxydized silver sleeve-buttons, bearing the device of a dog's face – English pug. He carried a slim cane, surmounted with an English pug's head with red glass eyes. Under his arm he carried a German grammar – Otto's. His hair was short, straight, and smooth, and presently when he turned his head a moment, I saw that it was nicely parted behind. He took a cigarette out of a dainty box, stuck it into a meerschaum holder which he carried in a morocco case, and reached for my cigar. While he was lighting, I said:

'Yes – I am an American.'

'I knew it – I can always tell them. What ship did you come over in?'

'*Holsatia*.'

'We came in the *Batavia* – Cunard, you know. What kind of a passage did you have?'

'Tolerably rough.'

'So did we. Captain said he'd hardly ever seen it rougher. Where are you from?'

'New England.'

'So'm I. I'm from New Bloomfield. Anybody with you?'

'Yes – a friend.'

'Our whole family's along. It's awful slow, going around alone – don't you think so?'

'Rather slow.'

'Ever been over here before?'

'Yes.'

'I haven't. My first trip. But we've been all around – Paris and everywhere. I'm to enter Harvard next year. Studying German all the time, now. Can't enter till I know German. I know considerable French – I get along pretty well in Paris, or anywhere where they speak French. What hotel are you stopping at?'

'Schweitzerhof.'

'No! is that so? I never see you in the reception-room. I go to the reception-room a good deal of the time, because there's so many Americans there. I make lots of acquaintances. I know an American as soon as I see him – and so I speak to him and make his acquaintance. I like to be always making acquaintances – don't you?'

'Lord, yes!'

'You see it breaks up a trip like this, first rate. I never get bored on a trip like this, if I can make acquaintances and have somebody to talk to. But I think a trip like this would be an awful bore, if a body couldn't find anybody to get acquainted with and talk to on a trip like this. I'm fond of talking, ain't you?'

'Passionately.'

'Have you felt bored, on this trip?'

'Not all the time, part of it.'

'That's it! – you see you ought to go around and get acquainted, and talk. That's my way. That's the way I always do – I just go 'round, 'round, 'round, and talk, talk, talk – I never get bored. You been up the Rigi yet?'

'No.'

'Going?'

'I think so.'

'What hotel you going to stop at?'

'I don't know. Is there more than one?'

'Three. You stop at the Schreiber – you'll find it full of Americans. What ship did you say you came over in?'

'*City of Antwerp.*'

'German, I guess. You going to Geneva?'

'Yes.'

'What hotel you going to stop at?'

'Hotel de l'Écu de Génève.'

'Don't you do it! No Americans there! You stop at one of those big hotels over the bridge – they're packed full of Americans.'

'But I want to practice my Arabic.'

'Good gracious, do you speak Arabic?'

'Yes – well enough to get along.'

'Why, hang it, you won't get along in Geneva – *they* don't speak Arabic, they speak French. What hotel are you stopping at here?'

'Hotel Pension-Beaurivage.'

'Sho, you ought to stop at the Schweitzerhof. Didn't you know the Schweitzerhof was the best hotel in Switzerland? – look at your Baedeker.'

'Yes, I know – but I had an idea there warn't any Americans there.'

'No Americans! Why, bless your soul, it's just alive with them! I'm in the great reception-room most all the time. I make lots of acquaintances there. Not as many as I did at first, because now only the new ones stop in there – the others go right along through. Where are you from?'

'Arkansas.'

'Is that so? I'm from New England – New Bloomfield's my town when I'm at home. I'm having a mighty good time today, ain't you?'

'Divine.'

'That's what I call it. I like this knocking around, loose and easy, and making acquaintances and talking. I know an American, soon as I see him; so I go and speak to him and make his acquaintance. I ain't ever bored, on a trip like this, if I can make new acquaintances and talk. I'm awful fond of talking when I can get hold of the right kind of a person, ain't you?'

'I prefer it to any other dissipation.'

'That's my notion, too. Now some people like to take a book and sit down and read, and read, and read, or moon around yawping at the lake or these mountains and things, but that ain't my way; no, sir, if they like it, let 'em do it, I don't object; but as for me, talking's what *I* like. You been up the Rigi?'

'Yes.'

'What hotel did you stop at?'

'Schreiber.'

'That's the place! – I stopped there too. *Full* of Americans, *wasn't* it? It always is – always is. That's what they say. Everybody says that. What ship did you come over in?'

'*Ville de Paris.*'

'French, I reckon. What kind of a passage did . . . excuse me a minute, there's some Americans I haven't seen before.'

And away he went. He went uninjured, too – I had the murderous impulse to harpoon him in the back with my alpenstock, but as I raised the weapon the disposition left me; I found I hadn't the heart to kill him, he was such a joyous, innocent, good-natured numbskull.

Half an hour later I was sitting on a bench inspecting, with strong interest, a noble monolith which we were skimming by – a monolith not shaped by man, but by Nature's free great hand – a massy pyramidal rock eighty feet high, devised by Nature ten million years ago against the day when a man worthy of it should need it for his monument. The time came at last, and now this grand remembrancer bears Schiller's name in huge letters upon its face. Curiously enough, this rock was not degraded or defiled in any way. It is said that two years ago a stranger let himself down from the top of it with ropes and pulleys, and painted all over it, in blue letters bigger than those in Schiller's name, these words:

TRY SOZODONT;

BUY SUN STOVE POLISH;

HELMBOLD'S BUCHU;

TRY BENZALINE FOR THE BLOOD.

He was captured, and it turned out that he was an American. Upon his trial the judge said to him:

'You are from a land where any insolent that wants to is privileged to profane and insult Nature, and, through her, Nature's God, if by so doing he can put a sordid penny in his pocket. But here the case is different. Because you are a foreigner and ignorant, I will make your sentence light; if you were a native I would deal strenuously with you. Hear and obey: You will immediately remove every trace of your offensive work from the Schiller monument; you will pay a fine of ten thousand francs; you will suffer two years' imprisonment at hard labor; you will then be horsewhipped, tarred and feathered, deprived of your ears, ridden on a rail to the confines of the canton, and banished forever. The severest penalties are omitted in your case – not as a grace to you, but to that great republic which had the misfortune to give you birth.'

The steamer's benches were ranged back to back across the deck. My back hair was mingling innocently with the back hair of a couple of ladies. Presently they were addressed by someone and I overheard this conversation:

'You are Americans, I think? So'm I.'

'Yes – we are Americans.'

'I knew it – I can always tell them. What ship did you come over in?'

'*City of Chester*.'

'Oh, yes – Inman line. We came in the *Batavia* – Cunard, you know. What kind of a passage did you have?'

'Pretty fair.'

'That was luck. We had it awful rough. Captain said he'd hardly ever seen it rougher. Where are you from?'

'New Jersey.'

'So'm I. No – I didn't mean that; I'm from New England. New Bloomfield's my place. These your children? – belong to both of you?'

'Only to one of us; they are mine; my friend is not married.'

'Single, I reckon? So'm I. Are you two ladies traveling alone?'

'No – my husband is with us.'

'Our whole family's along. It's awful slow, going around alone – don't you think so?'

164

'I suppose it must be.'

'Hi, there's Mount Pilatus coming in sight again. Named after Pontius Pilate, you know, that shot the apple off of William Tell's head. Guide-book tells all about it, they say. I didn't read it – an American told me. I don't read when I'm knocking around like this, having a good time. Did you ever see the chapel where William Tell used to preach?'

'I did not know he ever preached there.'

'Oh, yes, he did. That American told me so. He don't ever shut up his guide-book. He knows more about this lake than the fishes in it. Besides, they *call* it "Tell's Chapel" – you know that yourself. You ever been over here before?'

'Yes.'

'I haven't. It's my first trip. But we've been all around – Paris and everywhere. I'm to enter Harvard next year. Studying German all the time now. Can't enter till I know German. This book's Otto's grammar. It's a mighty good book to get the *ich habe gehabt habens* out of. But I don't really study when I'm knocking around this way. If the notion takes me, I just run over my little old *ich habe gehabt, du hast gehabt, er hat gehabt, wir haben gehabt, ihr haben gehabt, sie haben gehabt* – kind of "Now-I-lay-me-down-to-sleep" fashion, you know, and after that, maybe I don't buckle to it again for three days. It's awful undermining to the intellect, German is; you want to take it in small doses, or first you know your brains all run together, and you feel them sloshing around in your head same as so much drawn butter. But French is different; *French* ain't anything. I ain't any more afraid of French than a tramp's afraid of pie; I can rattle off my little *j'ai, tu as, il a*, and the rest of it, just as easy as a-b-c. I get along pretty well in Paris, or anywhere where they speak French. What hotel are you stopping at?'

'The Schweitzerhof.'

'No! is that so? I never see you in the big reception-room. I go in there a good deal of the time, because there's so many Americans there. I make lots of acquaintances. You been up the Rigi yet?'

'No.'

'Going?'

'We think of it.'

'What hotel you going to stop at?'

'I don't know.'

'Well, then, you stop at the Schreiber – it's full of Americans. What ship did you come over in?'

'*City of Chester.*'

'Oh, yes, I remember I asked you that before. But I always ask everybody what ship they came over in, and so sometimes I forget and ask again. You going to Geneva?'

'Yes.'

'What hotel you going to stop at?'

'We expect to stop in a pension.'

'I don't hardly believe you'll like that; there's very few Americans in the pensions. What hotel are you stopping at here?'

'The Schweitzerhof.'

'Oh, yes, I asked you that before, too. But I always ask everybody what hotel they're stopping at, and so I've got my head all mixed up with hotels. But it makes talk, and I love to talk. It refreshes me up so – don't it you – on a trip like this?'

'Yes – sometimes.'

'Well, it does me, too. As long as I'm talking I never feel bored – ain't that the way with you?'

'Yes – generally. But there are exceptions to the rule.'

'Oh, of course. *I* don't care to talk to everybody, *myself*. If a person starts in to jabber-jabber-jabber about scenery, and history, and pictures, and all sorts of tiresome things, I get the fan-tods mighty soon. I say "Well, I must be going now – hope I'll see you again" – and then I take a walk. Where you from?'

'New Jersey.'

'Why, bother it all, I asked you *that* before, too. Have you seen the Lion of Lucerne?'

'Not yet.'

'Nor I, either. But the man who told me about Mount Pilatus says it's one of the things to see. It's twenty-eight feet long. It don't seem reasonable, but he said so, anyway. He saw it yesterday; said it was dying, then, so I reckon it's dead by this time. But that ain't any matter, of course they'll stuff it. Did you say the children are yours – or *hers*?'

'Mine.'

'Oh, so you did. Are you going up the . . . no, I asked you

166

that. What ship . . . no, I asked you that, too. What hotel are you . . . no, you told me that. Let me see . . . um. . . . Oh, what kind of a voy . . . no, we've been over that ground, too. Um . . . um . . . well, I believe that is all. *Bonjour* – I am very glad to have made your acquaintance, ladies. *Guten Tag*.'

A Tramp Abroad

Guying the Guides

I used to worship the mighty genius of Michael Angelo – that man who was great in poetry, painting, sculpture, architecture – great in everything he undertook. But I do not want Michael Angelo for breakfast – for luncheon – for dinner – for tea – for supper – for between meals. I like a change, occasionally. In Genoa, he designed everything; in Milan he or his pupils designed everything; he designed the Lake of Como; in Padua, Verona, Venice, Bologna, who did we ever hear of, from guides, but Michael Angelo? In Florence, he painted everything, designed everything, nearly, and what he did not design he used to sit on a favorite stone and look at, and they showed us the stone. In Pisa he designed everything but the old shot-tower, and they would have attributed that to him if it had not been so awfully out of the perpendicular. He designed the piers of Leghorn and the custom-house regulations of Civita Vecchia. But, here – here it is frightful. He designed St Peter's; he designed the Pope; he designed the Pantheon, the uniform of the Pope's soldiers, the Tiber, the Vatican, the Colosseum, the Capitol, the Tarpeian Rock, the Barberini Palace, St John Lateran, the Campagna, the Appian Way, the Seven Hills, the Baths of Caracalla, the Claudian Aqueduct, the Cloaca Maxima – the eternal bore designed the Eternal City, and unless all men and books do lie, he painted everything in it! Dan said the other day to the guide, 'Enough, enough, enough! Say no more! Lump the whole thing! Say that the Creator made Italy from designs by Michael Angelo!'

I never felt so fervently thankful, so soothed, so tranquil, so filled with a blessed peace, as I did yesterday when I learned that Michael Angelo was dead.

But we have taken it out of this guide. He has marched us through miles of pictures and sculpture in the vast corridors of the Vatican; and through miles of pictures and sculpture in twenty other palaces; he has shown us the great picture in the Sistine Chapel, and frescos enough to fresco the heavens – pretty much all done by Michael Angelo. So with him we have played that game which has vanquished so many guides for us – imbecility and idiotic questions. These creatures never suspect – they have no idea of a sarcasm.

He shows us a figure and says: 'Statoo brunzo.' (Bronze statue.)

We look at it indifferently and the doctor asks: 'By Michael Angelo?'

'No – not know who.'

Then he shows us the ancient Roman Forum. The doctor asks: 'Michael Angelo?'

A stare from the guide. 'No – a thousan' year before he is born.'

Then an Egyptian obelisk. Again: 'Michael Angelo?'

'Oh, *mon dieu*, genteelmen! Zis is *two* thousan' year before he is born!'

He grows so tired of that unceasing question sometimes, that he dreads to show us anything at all. The wretch has tried all the ways he can think of to make us comprehend that Michael Angelo is only responsible for the creation of a *part* of the world, but somehow he has not succeeded yet. Relief for overtasked eyes and brain from study and sight-seeing is necessary, or we shall become idiotic sure enough. Therefore this guide must continue to suffer. If he does not enjoy it, so much the worse for him. We do.

In this place I may as well jot down a chapter concerning those necessary nuisances, European guides. Many a man has wished in his heart he could do without his guide; but knowing he could not, has wished he could get some amusement out of him as a remuneration for the affliction of his society. We accomplished this latter matter, and if our experience can be made useful to others they are welcome to it.

Guides know about enough English to tangle everything up so that a man can make neither head nor tail of it. They know their story by heart – the history of every statue, painting, cathedral, or other wonder they show you. They know it and tell it as a parrot would – and if you interrupt, and throw them off the track, they have to go back and begin over again. All their lives long, they are employed in showing strange things to foreigners and listening to their bursts of admiration. It is human nature to take delight in exciting admiration. It is what prompts children to say 'smart' things, and do absurd ones, and in other ways 'show off' when company is present. It is what makes gossips turn out in rain and storm to go and be the first to tell a startling bit of news. Think, then, what a passion it becomes with a guide, whose privilege it is, every day, to show to strangers wonders that throw them into perfect ecstasies of admiration! He gets so that he could not by any possibility live in a soberer atmosphere. After we discovered this, we *never* went into ecstasies any more – we never admired anything – we never showed any but impassible faces and stupid indifference in the presence of the sublimest wonders a guide had to display. We had found their weak point. We have made good use of it ever since. We have made some of those people savage, at times, but we have never lost our own serenity.

The doctor asks the questions, generally, because he can keep his countenance, and look more like an inspired idiot, and throw more imbecility into the tone of his voice than any man that lives. It comes natural to him.

The guides in Genoa are delighted to secure an American party, because Americans so much wonder, and deal so much in sentiment and emotion before any relic of Columbus. Our guide there fidgeted about as if he had swallowed a spring mattress. He was full of animation – full of impatience. He said:

'Come wis me, genteelmen – come! I show you ze letter-writing by Christopher Colombo – write it himself – write it wis his own hand – come!'

He took us to the municipal palace. After much impressive fumbling of keys and opening of locks, the stained and aged document was spread before us. The guide's eyes sparkled. He danced about us and tapped the parchment with his finger:

'What I tell you, genteelmen! Is it not so? See! handwriting Christopher Colombo! – write it himself!'

We looked indifferent – unconcerned. The doctor examined the document very deliberately, during a painful pause. Then he said, without any show of interest:

'Ah – Ferguson – what – what did you say was the name of the party who wrote this?'

'Christopher Colombo! ze great Christopher Colombo!'
Another deliberate examination.

'Ah – did he write it himself, or – or how?'

'He write it himself – Christopher Colombo! he's own hand-writing, write by himself!'

Then the doctor laid the document down and said:

'Why, I have seen boys in America only fourteen years old that could write better than that.'

'But zis is ze great Christo—'

'I don't care who it is! It's the worst writing I ever saw. Now you mustn't think you can impose on us because we are strangers. We are not fools, by a good deal. If you have got any specimens of penmanship of real merit, trot them out – and if you haven't, drive on!'

We drove on. The guide was considerably shaken up, but he made one more venture. He had something which he thought would overcome us. He said:

'Ah, genteelmen, you come wis me! I show you beautiful, oh, magnificent bust Christopher Colombo – splendid, grand, magnificent!'

He brought us before the beautiful bust – for it *was* beautiful – and sprang back and struck an attitude:

'Ah, look, genteelmen – beautiful, grand – bust Christopher Colombo! – beautiful bust, beautiful pedestal!'

The doctor put up his eyeglass – procured for such occasions:

'Ah – what did you say this gentleman's name was?'

'Christopher Colombo – ze great Christopher Colombo!'

'Christopher Colombo – the great Christopher Colombo. Well, what did *he* do?'

'Discover America! – discover America, oh, ze devil!'

'Discover America. No – that statement will hardly wash. We are just from America ourselves. We heard nothing about it. Christopher Colombo – pleasant name – is – is he dead?'

'Oh, *corpo di Baccho* – three hundred year!'

'What did he die of?'

'I do not know – I cannot tell.'

'Smallpox, think?'

'I do not know, genteelmen! – I do not know *what* he die of!'

'Measles, likely?'

'Maybe – maybe – I do *not* know – I think he die of some-things.'

'Parents living?'

'Im-posseeble!'

'Ah – which is the bust and which is the pedestal?'

'Santa Maria! – *zis* ze bust – *zis* ze pedestal!'

'Ah, I see, I see – happy combination – very happy combination, indeed. Is – is this the first time this gentleman was ever on a bust?'

That joke was lost on the foreigner – guides cannot master the subtleties of the American joke.

We have made it interesting for this Roman guide. Yesterday we spent three or four hours in the Vatican again, that wonderful world of curiosities. We came very near expressing interest, sometimes – even admiration – it was very hard to keep from it. We succeeded though. Nobody else ever did, in the Vatican museums. The guide was bewildered – nonplussed. He walked his legs off, nearly, hunting up extraordinary things, and exhausted all his ingenuity on us, but it was a failure; we never showed any interest in anything. He had reserved what he considered to be his greatest wonder till the last – a royal Egyptian mummy, the best-preserved in the world, perhaps. He took us there. He felt so sure, this time, that some of his old enthusiasm came back to him:

'See, genteelmen! – Mummy! Mummy!'

The eyeglass came up as calmly, as deliberately as ever.

'Ah – Ferguson – what did I understand you to say the gentleman's name was?'

'Name? – he got no name – Mummy! – 'Gyptian mummy!'

'Yes, yes. Born here?'

'No! *'Gyptian* mummy!'

'Ah, just so. Frenchman, I presume?'

'No! – *not* Frenchman, not Roman! – born in Egypt!'

'Born in Egypta. Never heard of Egypta before. Foreign locality, likely. Mummy – mummy. How calm he is – how self-possessed. Is, ah – is he dead?'

'Oh, *sacré bleu*, been dead three thousan' year!'

The doctor turned on him savagely:

'Here, now, what do you mean by such conduct as this! Play-

172

ing us for Chinamen because we are strangers and trying to learn! Trying to impose your vile second-hand carcasses on *us* – thunder and lightning, I've a notion to – to – if you've got a nice *fresh* corpse, fetch him out! – or, by George, we'll brain you!'

We make it exceedingly interesting for this Frenchman. However, he has paid us back, partly, without knowing it. He came to the hotel this morning to ask if we were up, and he endeavored as well as he could to describe us, so that the land-lord would know which persons he meant. He finished with the casual remark that we were lunatics. The observation was so innocent and so honest that it amounted to a very good thing for a guide to say.

There is one remark (already mentioned) which never yet has failed to disgust these guides. We use it always, when we can think of nothing else to say. After they have exhausted their enthusiasm pointing out to us and praising the beauties of some ancient bronze image or broken-legged statue, we look at it stupidly and in silence for five, ten, fifteen minutes – as long as we can hold out, in fact – and then ask:

'Is – is he dead?'

That conquers the serenest of them. It is not what they are looking for – especially a new guide. Our Roman Ferguson is the most patient, unsuspecting, long-suffering subject we have had yet. We shall be sorry to part with him. We have enjoyed his society very much. We trust he has enjoyed ours, but we are harassed with doubts.

The Innocents Abroad

Ascending Mont Blanc

After breakfast, that next morning in Chamonix, we went out in the yard and watched the gangs of excursionizing tourists arriving and departing with their mules and guides and porters; then we took a look through the telescope at the snowy hump of Mont Blanc. It was brilliant with sunshine, and the vast smooth bulge seemed hardly five hundred yards away. With the naked eye we could dimly make out the house at the Pierre Pointue, which is located by the side of the great glacier, and is more than 3,000 feet above the level of the valley, but with the telescope we could see all its details. While I looked, a woman rode by the house on a mule, and I saw her with sharp distinctness; I could have described her dress. I saw her nod to the people of the house, and rein up her mule, and put her hand up to shield her eyes from the sun. I was not used to telescopes; in fact, I never had looked through a good one before; it seemed incredible to me that this woman could be so far away. I was satisfied that I could see all these details with my naked eye; but when I tried it, that mule and those vivid people had wholly vanished, and the house itself had become small and vague. I tried the telescope again, and again everything was vivid. The strong black shadows of the mule and the woman were flung against the side of the house, and I saw the mule's silhouette wave its ears.

The telescopulist – or the telescopulariat – I do not know which is right – said a party were making the grand ascent, and would come in sight on the remote upper heights, presently; so we waited to observe this performance.

Presently I had a superb idea. I wanted to stand with a party on the summit of Mont Blanc, merely to be able to say I had done it, and I believed the telescope could set me within seven feet of the uppermost man. The telescoper assured me that it could. I then asked him how much I owed him for as far as I had got? He said, one franc. I asked him how much it would cost me to make the entire ascent? Three francs. I at once determined to make the entire ascent. But first I inquired if there was any danger? He said no – not by telescope; said he had taken a great many parties to the summit, and never lost a man. I asked what he would charge to let my agent go with me, together with such guides and porters as might be necessary? He said he would let Harris go for two francs; and that unless we were unusually timid, he should consider guides and porters unnecessary, it was not customary to take them when going by telescope, for they were rather an incumbrance than a help. He said that the party now on the mountain were approaching the most difficult part, and if we hurried we should overtake them within ten minutes, and could then join them and have the benefit of their guides and porters without their knowledge, and without expense to us.

I then said we would start immediately. I believe I said it calmly, though I was conscious of a shudder and of a paling cheek, in view of the nature of the exploit I was so unreflectingly engaging in. But the old dare-devil spirit was upon me, and I said that as I had committed myself, I would not back down; I would ascend Mont Blanc if it cost me my life. I told the man to slant his machine in the proper direction, and let us be off.

Harris was afraid and did not want to go, but I heartened him up and said I would hold his hand all the way; so he gave his consent, though he trembled a little at first. I took a last pathetic look upon the pleasant summer scene about me, then boldly put my eye to the glass and prepared to mount among the grim glaciers and the everlasting snows.

We took our way carefully and cautiously across the great Glacier des Bossons, over yawning and terrific crevasses and amongst imposing crags and buttresses of ice, which were fringed with icicles of gigantic proportions. The desert of ice that stretched far and wide about us was wild and desolate beyond description, and the perils which beset us were so great that at times I was minded to turn back. But I pulled my pluck together and pushed on.

We passed the glacier safely and began to mount the steeps beyond, with great celerity. When we were seven minutes out from the starting-point, we reached an altitude where the scene took a new aspect; an apparently limitless continent of gleaming snow was tilted heavenward before our faces. As my eye followed that awful acclivity far away up into the remote skies, it seemed to me that all I had ever seen before of sublimity and

175

magnitude was small and insignificant compared with this.

We rested a moment, and then began to mount with speed. Within three minutes we caught sight of the party ahead of us, and stopped to observe them. They were toiling up a long, slanting ridge of snow – twelve persons, roped together some fifteen feet apart, marching in single file, and strongly marked against the clear blue sky. One was a woman. We could see them lift their feet and put them down; we saw them swing their alpenstocks forward in unison, like so many pendulums, and then bear their weight upon them; we saw the lady wave her handkerchief. They dragged themselves upwards in a worn and weary way, for they had been climbing steadily from the Grands Mulets, on the Glacier des Bossons, since three in the morning, and it was eleven now. We saw them sink down in the snow and rest, and drink something from a bottle. After a while they moved on, and as they approached the final short dash of the home stretch we closed up on them and joined them.

Presently we all stood together on the summit! What a view was spread out below! Away off under the north-western horizon rolled the silent billows of the Farnese Oberland, their snowy crests glinting softly in the subdued lights of distance; in the north rose the giant form of the Wobblehorn, draped from peak to shoulder in sable thunder-clouds; beyond him, to the right, stretched the grand processional summits of the Cisalpine Cordillera, drowned in a sensuous haze; to the east loomed the colossal masses of the Yodelhorn, the Fuddlehorn, and the Dinnerhorn, their cloudless summits flashing white and cold in the sun; beyond them shimmered the faint far line of the Ghauts of Jubbulpore and the Aiguilles des Alleghenies; in the south towered the smoking peak of Popocatapetl and the unapproachable altitudes of the peerless Scrabblehorn; in the west-south-west the stately range of the Himalayas lay dreaming in a purple gloom; and thence all around the curving horizon the eye roved over a troubled sea of sun-kissed Alps, and noted here and there the noble proportions and soaring domes of the Bottlehorn, and the Saddlehorn, and the Shovelhorn, and the Powderhorn, all bathed in the glory of noon, and mottled with softly gliding blots, the shadows flung from drifting clouds.

Overcome by the scene, we all raised a triumphant, tremendous shout, in unison. A startled man at my elbow said:

'Confound you, what do you yell like that for, right here in the street?'

That brought me down to Chamonix like a flirt. I gave that man some spiritual advice and disposed of him, and then paid the telescope man his full fee, and said that we were charmed with the trip, and would remain down, and not re-ascend and require him to fetch us down by telescope. This pleased him very much, for of course we could have stepped back to the summit and put him to the trouble of bringing us home if we had wanted to.

A Tramp Abroad

European Food

A man accustomed to American food and American domestic cookery would not starve to death suddenly in Europe; but I think he would gradually waste away, and eventually die.

He would have to do without his accustomed morning meal. That is too formidable a change altogether; he would necessarily suffer from it. He could get the shadow, the sham, the base counterfeit of that meal; but that would do him no good, and money could not buy the reality.

To particularize: the average American's simplest and commonest form of breakfast consists of coffee and beefsteak; well, in Europe, coffee is an unknown beverage. You can get what the European hotel-keeper thinks is coffee, but it resembles the real thing as hypocrisy resembles holiness. It is a feeble, characterless, uninspiring sort of stuff, and almost as undrinkable as if it had been made in an American hotel. The milk used for it is what the French call 'Christian' milk – milk which has been baptized.

After a few months' acquaintance with European 'coffee', one's mind weakens, and his faith with it, and he begins to wonder if the rich beverage of home, with its clotted layer of yellow cream on top of it, is not a mere dream after all, and a thing which never existed.

Next comes the European bread – fair enough, good enough, after a fashion, but cold; cold and tough, and unsympathetic; and never any change, never any variety – always the same tiresome thing.

Next, the butter – the sham and tasteless butter; no salt in it, and made of goodness knows what.

Then there is the beefsteak. They have it in Europe, but they don't know how to cook it. Neither will they cut it right. It comes on the table in a small, round, pewter platter. It lies in the center of this platter, in a bordering bed of grease-soaked potatoes; it is the size, shape, and thickness of a man's hand with the thumb and fingers cut off. It is a little overdone, is rather dry, it tastes pretty insipidly, it rouses no enthusiasm.

Imagine a poor exile contemplating that inert thing; and imagine an angel suddenly sweeping down out of a better land and setting before him a mighty porter-house steak an inch and a half thick, hot and sputtering from the griddle; dusted with fragrant pepper; enriched with little melting bits of butter of the most unimpeachable freshness and genuineness; the precious juices of the meat trickling out and joining the gravy, archipel-agoed with mushrooms; a township or two of tender, yellowish fat gracing an outlying district of this ample county of beefsteak; the long white bone which divides the sirloin from the tender-loin still in its place; and imagine that the angel also adds a great cup of American home-made coffee, with the cream a-froth on top, some real butter, firm and yellow and fresh, some smoking hot biscuits, a plate of hot buckwheat cakes, with transparent syrup – could words describe the gratitude of this exile?

The European dinner is better than the European breakfast, but it has its faults and inferiorities; it does not satisfy. He comes to the table eager and hungry; he swallows his soup – there is an undefinable lack about it somewhere; thinks the fish is going to be the thing he wants – eats it and isn't sure; thinks the next dish is perhaps the one that will hit the hungry place – tries it, and is conscious that there was a something wanting about it also. And thus he goes on, from dish to dish, like a boy after a butterfly, which just misses getting caught every time it alights, but somehow doesn't get caught after all; and at the end the exile and the boy have fared about alike; the one is full, but grievously unsatisfied, the other has had plenty of exercise, plenty of interest, and a fine lot of hopes, but he hasn't got any butterfly. There is here and there an American who will say he can remember rising from a European *table d'hôte* perfectly satis-fied; but we must not overlook the fact that there is also here and there an American who will lie.

The number of dishes is sufficient; but then it is such a monotonous variety of *unstriking* dishes. It is an inane dead level of 'fair-to-middling'. There is nothing to *accent* it. Perhaps if the roast of mutton or of beef – a big generous one – were brought on the table and carved in full view of the client, that might give the right sense of earnestness and reality to the thing; but they don't do that, they pass the sliced meat around on a dish, and so you are perfectly calm, it does not stir you in the least. Now a vast roast turkey, stretched on the broad of his back, with his heels in the air and the rich juices oozing from his fat sides . . . But I may as well stop there, for they would not know how to cook him. They can't even cook a chicken respectably; and as for carving it, they do that with a hatchet.

This is about the customary *table d'hôte* bill in summer:

Soup (characterless).

Fish – sole, salmon, or whiting – usually tolerably good.

Roast – mutton or beef – tasteless – and some last year's potatoes.

A pâté, or some other made-dish – usually good – 'considering'.

One vegetable – brought on in state, and all alone – usually insipid lentils, or string beans, or indifferent asparagus.

Roast chicken, as tasteless as paper.

Lettuce-salad – tolerably good.

Decayed strawberries or cherries.

Sometimes the apricots and figs are fresh, but this is no advantage, as these fruits are of no account anyway.

The grapes are generally good, and sometimes there is a tolerably good peach, by mistake.

The variations of the above bill are trifling. After a fortnight one discovers that the variations are only apparent, not real; in the third week you get what you had the first, and in the fourth week you get what you had the second. Three or four months of this weary sameness will kill the robustest appetite.

It has now been many months, at the present writing, since I have had a nourishing meal, but I shall soon have one – a modest, private affair, all to myself. I have selected a few dishes, and made out a little bill of fare, which will go home in the steamer that precedes me, and be hot when I arrive – as follows:

Radishes. Baked apples, with cream.
Fried oysters; stewed oysters. Frogs.
American coffee, with real cream.
American butter.
Fried chicken, Southern style.
Porter-house steak.

Saratoga potatoes.
Broiled chicken, American style.
Hot biscuits, Southern style.
Hot wheat-bread, Southern style.
Hot buckwheat cakes.
American toast. Clear maple syrup.
Virginia bacon, broiled.
Blue-points, on the half shell.
Cherry-stone clams.
San Francisco mussels, steamed.
Oyster soup. Clam soup.
Philadelphia Terrapin soup.
Oysters roasted in shell, Northern style.
Soft-shell crabs. Connecticut shad.
Baltimore perch.
Brook trout, from Sierra Nevadas.
Lake trout, from Tahoe.
Sheep-head and croakers, from New Orleans.
Black bass from the Mississippi.
American roast beef.
Roast turkey, Thanksgiving style.
Cranberry sauce. Celery.
Roast wild turkey. Woodcock.
Canvas-back duck, from Baltimore.
Prairie hens, from Illinois.
Missouri partridges, broiled.
'Possum. Coon.
Boston bacon and beans.
Bacon and greens, Southern style.
Hominy. Boiled onions. Turnips.
Pumpkin. Squash. Asparagus.
Butter beans. Sweet potatoes.
Lettuce. Succotash. String beans.
Mashed potatoes. Catsup.
Boiled potatoes, in their skins.
New potatoes, minus the skins.
Early Rose potatoes, roasted in the ashes, Southern style, served hot.
Sliced tomatoes, with sugar or vinegar. Stewed tomatoes.
Green corn, cut from the ear and served with butter and pepper.

Green corn, on the ear.
Hot corn-pone, with chitlings, Southern style.
Hot hoe-cake, Southern style.
Hot egg-bread, Southern style.
Hot light-bread, Southern style.
Buttermilk. Iced sweet milk.
Apple dumplings, with real cream.
Apple pie. Apple fritters.
Apple puffs, Southern style.
Peach cobbler, Southern style.
Peach pie. American mince pie.
Pumpkin pie. Squash pie.
All sorts of American pastry.
Fresh American fruits of all sorts, including strawberries, which are
not to be doled out as if they were jewelry, but in a more liberal way.
Ice-water – not prepared in the ineffectual goblet, but in the sincere
and capable refrigerator.

Americans intending to spend a year or so in European hotels, will do well to copy this bill and carry it along. They will find it an excellent thing to get up an appetite with, in the dispiriting presence of the squalid *table d'hôte*.

We read that Esaw sold out hiz birth rite for soup, and menny wonder at hiz extravegance, but Esaw diskovered arly, what menny a man haz diskovered since, that it iz hard work tew live on a pedigree.

If i waz starving, I wouldn't hesitate tew swap oph all the pedigree I had, and all mi relashuns had, for a quart of pottage, and throw two grate grandfathers into the bargain.

JOSH BILLINGS

Back from 'Yurrup'

Have you ever seen a family of geese just back from Europe – or Yurrup, as they pronounce it? They never talk *to* you, of course, being strangers, but they talk to each other and *at* you till you are pretty nearly distracted with their clatter; till you are sick of their ocean experiences; their mispronounced foreign names; their dukes and emperors; their trivial adventures; their point-less reminiscences; till you are sick of their imbecile faces and their relentless clack, and wish it had pleased Providence to leave the clapper out of their empty skulls.

I traveled with such a family one eternal day, from New York to Boston, last week. They had spent just a year in 'Yurrup', and were returning home to Boston. Papa said little, and looked bored – he had simply been down to New York to receive and cart home his cargo of traveled imbecility. Sister Angeline, aged twenty-three, sister Augusta, aged twenty-five, and brother Charles, aged thirty-three, did the conversational drivel, and Mamma purred and admired, and threw in some help when occasion offered, in the way of remembering some French bar-ber's – I should say some French Count's – name, when they pretended to have forgotten it. They occupied the choice seats in the parlor of the drawing-room car, and for twelve hours I sat opposite to them – was their *vis-à-vis*, they would have said, in their charming French way.

AUGUSTA: 'Plague that nahsty [nasty] steamer! I've the headache yet, she rolled so the fifth day out.'

ANGELINE: 'And well you may. *I* never saw such a nahsty old tub. I never want to go in the *Ville de Paris* again. Why *didn't* we go over to London and come in the *Scotia*?'

AUG.: 'Because we were fools!'

[I endorsed that sentiment.]

ANGIE: 'Gustie, what made Count Nixkumarouse drive off looking so blue, that last Thursday in Pairy? [Paris, she meant.] Ah, own up, now!' [*tapping her arm so roguishly with her ivory fan.*]

AUG.: 'Now, Angie, how you talk! I *told* the nahsty creature I would not receive his attentions any longer. And the old duke, his father, kept boring me about him and his two million francs a year till I sent *him* off with a flea in his ear.'

CHORUS: 'Ke-he-he! Ha-ha-ha!'

CHARLES [*pulling a small silken cloak to pieces*]: 'Angie, where'd you get this cheap thing?'

ANGIE: 'You, Cholly, let that alone! Cheap! Well, how could I help it? There we were, tied up in Switzerland – just down from Mon Blong [Mont Blanc, doubtless] – couldn't buy anything in those nahsty shops so far away from Pairy. I had to put up with that slimpsy forty-dollar rag – but bless you, I couldn't go naked!'

CHORUS: 'Ke-he-he!'

AUG.: 'Guess who I was thinking of? Those ignorant persons we saw first in Rome and afterwards in Venice – those—'

ANGIE: 'Oh, ha-ha-ha! He-he-he! It *was* so funny! Papa, one of them called the Santa della Spiggiola the Santa della Spizz-iola! Ha-ha-ha! And she thought it was Canova that did Michael Angelo's Moses! Only *think* of it – Canova, a sculptor, and the Moses a picture! I thought I should die! I guess I let them see by the way I laughed, that they'd made fools of themselves, because they blushed and sneaked off.'

[Papa laughed faintly, but not with the easy grace of a man who was certain he knew what he was laughing about.]

AUG.: 'Why, Cholly! Where did you get those nahsty Beaumarchais gloves? Well, I *wouldn't*, if I were you!'

MAMMA [*with uplifted hands*]: 'Beaumarchais, my son!'

ANGIE: 'Beaumarchais! Why how can you! Nobody in Pairy wears those nahsty things but the commonest people.'

CHARLES: 'They *are* a rum lot, but then Tom Blennerhasset gave 'em to me – he wanted to do something or other to curry favor, I s'pose.'

ANGIE: 'Tom Blennerhasset!'

AUG.: 'Tom Blennerhasset!'

MAMMA: 'Tom Blennerhasset! And have you been associating with *him*!'

PAPA [*suddenly interested*]: 'Heavens, what has the son of an honored and honorable old friend been doing?'

CHORUS: 'Doing! Why his father has endorsed himself bankrupt for friends – that's what's the matter!'

ANGIE: '*Oh, mon Dieu, j'ai faim! Avez-vous quelque chose de bon, en votre poche, mon cher frère?* Excuse me for speaking French, for, to tell the truth, I haven't spoken English for so long that it comes dreadful awkward. Wish we were back in Yurrup – *c'est votre désire aussi, n'est-ce pas, mes chères?*'

And from that moment they lapsed into barbarous French and kept it up for an hour – hesitating, gasping for words, stumbling head over heels through adverbs and participles, floundering among adjectives, working miracles of villainous pronunciation – and neither one of them by any chance ever understanding what another was driving at.

By that time some newcomers had entered the car, and so they lapsed into English again, and fell to holding everything American up to scorn and contumely in order that they might thus let those newcomers know they were just home from 'Yurrup'. To use their pet and best beloved phrase, they were a 'nahsty' family of American snobs, and there ought to be a law against allowing such to go to Europe and misrepresent the nation. It will take these insects five years, without doubt, to get done turning up their noses at everything American and making damaging comparisons between their own country and 'Yurrup'. Let us pity their waiting friends in Boston in their affliction.

The £1,000,000 Bank-Note

When I was twenty-seven years old, I was a mining-broker's clerk in San Francisco, and an expert in all the details of stock traffic. I was alone in the world, and had nothing to depend upon but my wits and a clean reputation; but these were setting my feet in the road to eventual fortune, and I was content with the prospect.

My time was my own after the afternoon board, Saturdays, and I was accustomed to put it in on a little sail-boat on the bay. One day I ventured too far, and was carried out to sea. Just at nightfall, when hope was about gone, I was picked up by a small brig which was bound for London. It was a long and stormy voyage, and they made me work my passage without pay, as a common sailor. When I stepped ashore in London my clothes were ragged and shabby, and I had only a dollar in my pocket. This money fed and sheltered me twenty-four hours. During the next twenty-four I went without food and shelter.

About ten o'clock on the following morning, seedy and hungry, I was dragging myself along Portland Place, when a child that was passing, towed by a nurse-maid, tossed a luscious big pear – minus one bite – into the gutter. I stopped, of course, and fastened my desiring eye on that muddy treasure. My mouth watered for it, my stomach craved it, my whole being begged for it. But every time I made a move to get it some passing eye detected my purpose, and of course I straightened up then, and looked indifferent, and pretended that I hadn't been thinking about the pear at all. This same thing kept happening and happening, and I couldn't get the pear. I was just getting desperate enough to brave all the shame, and to seize it, when a window behind me was raised, and a gentleman spoke out of it, saying:

'Step in here, please.'

I was admitted by a gorgeous flunkey, and shown into a sumptuous room where a couple of elderly gentlemen were sitting. They sent away the servant, and made me sit down. They had just finished their breakfast, and the sight of the remains of it almost overpowered me. I could hardly keep my wits together in the presence of that food, but as I was not asked to sample it, I had to bear my trouble as best I could.

Now, something had been happening there a little before, which I did not know anything about until a good many days afterward, but I will tell you about it now. Those two old brothers had been having a pretty hot argument a couple of days before, and had ended by agreeing to decide it by a bet, which is the English way of settling everything.

You will remember that the Bank of England once issued two notes of a million pounds each, to be used for a special purpose connected with some public transaction with a foreign country. For some reason or other only one of these had been used and canceled; the other still lay in the vaults of the Bank. Well, the brothers, chatting along, happened to get to wondering what might be the fate of a perfectly honest and intelligent stranger who should be turned adrift in London without a friend, and with no money but that million-pound bank-note, and no way to account for his being in possession of it. Brother A said he would starve to death; Brother B said he wouldn't. Brother A said he couldn't offer it at a bank or anywhere else, because he would be arrested on the spot. So they went on disputing till Brother B said he would bet twenty thousand pounds that the man would live thirty days, *anyway*, on that million, and keep out of jail, too. Brother A took him up. Brother B went down to the Bank and bought that note. Just like an Englishman, you see; pluck to the backbone. Then he dictated a letter, which one of his clerks wrote out in a beautiful round hand, and then the two brothers sat at the window a whole day watching for the right man to give it to.

They saw many honest faces go by that were not intelligent enough; many that were intelligent, but not honest enough; many that were both, but the possessors were not poor enough, or, if poor enough, were not strangers. There was always a defect, until I came along; but they agreed that I filled the bill all around; so they elected me unanimously, and there I was now waiting to know why I was called in. They began to ask me questions about myself, and pretty soon they had my story. Finally they told me I would answer their purpose. I said I was sincerely glad, and asked what it was. Then one of them handed me an

187

envelope, and said I would find the explanation inside. I was going to open it, but he said no; take it to my lodgings, and look it over carefully, and not be hasty or rash. I was puzzled, and wanted to discuss the matter a little further, but they didn't; so I took my leave, feeling hurt and insulted to be made the butt of what was apparently some kind of a practical joke, and yet obliged to put up with it, not being in circumstances to resent affronts from rich and strong folk.

I would have picked up the pear now and eaten it before all the world, but it was gone; so I had lost that by this unlucky business, and the thought of it did not soften my feeling toward those men. As soon as I was out of sight of that house I opened my envelope, and saw that it contained money! My opinion of those people changed, I can tell you! I lost not a moment, but shoved note and money into my vest pocket, and broke for the nearest cheap eating-house. Well, how I did eat! When at last I couldn't hold any more, I took out my money and unfolded it, took one glimpse and nearly fainted. Five millions of dollars! Why, it made my head swim.

I must have sat there stunned and blinking at the note as much as a minute before I came rightly to myself again. The first thing I noticed, then, was the landlord. His eye was on the note, and he was petrified. He was worshiping, with all his body and soul, but he looked as if he couldn't stir hand or foot. I took my cue in a moment, and did the only rational thing there was to do. I reached the note toward him, and said, carelessly:

'Give me the change, please.'

Then he was restored to his normal condition, and made a thousand apologies for not being able to break the bill, and I couldn't get him to touch it. He wanted to look at it, and keep on looking at it; he couldn't seem to get enough of it to quench the thirst of his eye, but he shrank from touching it as if it had been something too sacred for poor common clay to handle. I said:

'I am sorry if it is an inconvenience, but I must insist. Please change it; I haven't anything else.'

But he said that wasn't any matter; he was quite willing to let the trifle stand over till another time. I said I might not be in his neighborhood again for a good while; but he said it was of no consequence, he could wait, and, moreover, I could have any-thing I wanted, any time I chose, and let the account run as long as I pleased. He said he hoped he wasn't afraid to trust as rich a gentleman as I was, merely because I was of a merry disposition, and chose to play larks on the public in the matter of dress. By this time another customer was entering, and the landlord hinted to me to put the monster out of sight; then he bowed me all the way to the door, and I started straight for that house and those brothers, to correct the mistake which had been made before the police should hunt me up, and help me do it. I was pretty nervous; in fact, pretty badly frightened, though, of course, I was no way in fault; but I knew men well enough to know that when they find they've given a tramp a million-pound bill when they thought it was a one-pounder, they are in a frantic rage against *him* instead of quarreling with their own near-sightedness, as they ought. As I approached the house my excitement began to abate, for all was quiet there, which made me feel pretty sure the blunder was not discovered yet. I rang. The same servant appeared. I asked for those gentlemen.

'They are gone.' This in the lofty, cold way of that fellow's tribe.

'Gone? Gone where?'

'On a journey.'

'But whereabouts?'

'To the Continent, I think.'

'The Continent?'

'Yes, sir.'

'Which way – by what route?'

'I can't say, sir.'

'When will they be back?'

'In a month, they said.'

'A month! Oh, this is awful! Give me *some* sort of idea of how to get a word to them. It's of the last importance.'

'I can't, indeed. I've no idea where they've gone, sir.'

'Then I must see some member of the family.'

'Family's away, too; been abroad months – in Egypt and India, I think.'

'Man, there's been an immense mistake made. They'll be back before night. Will you tell them I've been here, and that I will keep coming till it's all made right, and they needn't be afraid?'

'I'll tell them, if they come back, but I am not expecting them. They said you would be here in an hour to make inquiries, but I must tell you it's all right, they'll be here on time and expect you.'

So I had to give it up and go away. What a riddle it all was! I was like to lose my mind. They would be here 'on time'. What could that mean? Oh the letter would explain, maybe. I had forgotten the letter; I got it out and read it. This is what it said:

You are an intelligent and honest man, as one may see by your face. We conceive you to be poor and a stranger. Enclosed you will find a sum of money. It is lent to you for thirty days, without interest. Report at this house at the end of that time. I have a bet on you. If I win it you shall have any situation that is in my gift – any, that is, that you shall be able to prove yourself familiar with and competent to fill.

No signature, no address, no date.

Well, here was a coil to be in! You are posted on what had preceded all this, but I was not. It was just a deep, dark puzzle to me. I hadn't the least idea what the game was, nor whether harm was meant me or a kindness. I went into a park, and sat down to try to think it out, and to consider what I had best do.

At the end of an hour my reasonings had crystallized into this verdict.

Maybe those men mean me well, maybe they mean me ill; no way to decide that – let it go. They've got a game, or a scheme, or an experiment, of some kind on hand; no way to determine what it is – let it go. There's a bet on me; no way to find out what it is – let it go. That disposes of the indeterminable quantities; the remainder of the matter is tangible, solid, and may be classed and labeled with certainty. If I ask the Bank of England to place this bill to the credit of the man it belongs to, they'll do it, for they know him, although I don't; but they will ask me how I came in possession of it, and if I tell the truth they'll put me in the asylum, naturally, and a lie will land me in jail. The same result would follow if I tried to bank the bill anywhere or to borrow money on it. I have got to carry this immense burden around until those men come back, whether I want to or not. It is useless to me, as useless as a handful of ashes, and yet I must take care of it, and watch over it, while I beg my living. I couldn't *give* it away, if I should try, for neither honest citizen nor highwayman would accept it or meddle with it for anything. Those brothers are safe. Even if I lose their bill, or burn it, they are still safe, because they can stop payment, and the bank will make them whole; but meantime I've got to do a month's suffering without wages or profit – unless I help win that bet, whatever it may be, and get that situation that I am promised. I *should* like to get that; men of their sort have situations in their gift that are worth having.

I got to thinking a good deal about that situation. My hopes began to rise high. Without doubt the salary would be large. It would begin in a month; after that I should be all right. Pretty soon I was feeling first rate. By this time I was tramping the streets again. The sight of a tailor-shop gave me a sharp longing to shed my rags, and to clothe myself decently once more. Could I afford it? No; I had nothing in the world but a million pounds. So I forced myself to go on by. But soon I was drifting back again. The temptation persecuted me cruelly. I must have passed that shop back and forth six times during that manful struggle. At last I gave in; I had to. I asked if they had a misfit suit that had been thrown on their hands. The fellow I spoke to nodded his head toward another fellow, and gave me no answer. I went to the indicated fellow, and he indicated another fellow with *his* head, and no words. I went to him, and he said:

' 'Tend to you presently.'

I waited till he was done with what he was at, then he took me into a back room, and overhauled a pile of rejected suits, and selected the rattiest one for me. I put it on. It didn't fit, and wasn't in any way attractive, but it was new, and I was anxious to have it; so I didn't find any fault, but said, with some diffidence:

'It would be an accommodation to me if you could wait some days for the money. I haven't any small change about me.'

The fellow worked up a most sarcastic expression of countenance, and said:

'Oh, you haven't? Well, of course, I didn't expect it. I'd only expect gentlemen like you to carry large change.'

I was nettled, and said:

'My friend, you shouldn't judge a stranger always by the clothes he wears. I am quite able to pay for this suit; I simply didn't wish to put you to the trouble of changing a large note.'

He modified his style a little at that, and said, though still with something of an air:

'I didn't mean any particular harm, but as long as rebukes are going, I might say it wasn't quite your affair to jump to the conclusion that we couldn't change any note that you might happen to be carrying around. On the contrary, we *can*.'

I handed the note to him, and said:

'Oh, very well; I apologize.'

He received it with a smile, one of those large smiles which go all around over, and have folds in them, and wrinkles, and spirals, and look like the place where you have thrown a brick in a pond; and then in the act of his taking a glimpse of the bill this smile froze solid, and turned yellow, and looked like those wavy, wormy spreads of lava which you find hardened on little levels on the side of Vesuvius. I never before saw a smile caught like that, and perpetuated. The man stood there holding the bill, and looking like that, and the proprietor hustled up to see what was the matter, and said, briskly:

'Well, what's up? what's the trouble? what's wanting?'

I said: 'There isn't any trouble. I'm waiting for my change.'

'Come, come; get him his change, Tod; get him his change.'

Tod retorted: 'Get him his change! It's easy to say, sir; but look at the bill yourself.'

The proprietor took a look, gave a low, eloquent whistle, then made a dive for the pile of rejected clothing, and began to snatch it this way and that, talking all the time excitedly, and as if to himself:

'Sell an eccentric millionaire such an unspeakable suit as that! Tod's a fool – a born fool. Always doing something like this. Drives every millionaire away from this place, because he can't tell a millionaire from a tramp, and never could. Ah, here's the thing I am after. Please get those things off, sir, and throw them in the fire. Do me the favor to put on this shirt and this suit; it's just the thing, the very thing – plain, rich, modest, and

just ducally nobby; màde to order for a foreign prince – you may know him, sir, his Serene Highness the Hospodar of Halifax; had to leave it with us and take a mourning-suit because his mother was going to die – which she didn't. But that's all right; we can't always have things the way we – that is, the way they – there! trousers all right, they fit you to a charm, sir; now the waistcoat; aha, right again! now the coat – lord! look at that, now! Perfect – the whole thing! I never saw such a triumph in all my experience.'

I expressed my satisfaction.

'Quite right, sir, quite right; it'll do for a makeshift, I'm bound to say. But wait till you see what we'll get up for you on your own measure. Come, Tod, book and pen; get at it. Length of leg, thirty-two inches' – and so on. Before I could get in a word he had measured me, and was giving orders for dress-suits, morning suits, shirts, and all sorts of things. When I got a chance I said:

'But, my dear sir, I *can't* give these orders, unless you can wait indefinitely, or change the bill.'

'Indefinitely! It's a weak word, sir, a weak word. Eternally – *that's* the word, sir. Tod, rush these things through, and send them to the gentleman's address without any waste of time. Let the minor customers wait. Set down the gentleman's address and—'

'I'm changing my quarters. I will drop in and leave the new address.'

'Quite right, sir, quite right. One moment – let me show you out, sir. There – good day, sir, good day.'

Well, don't you see what was bound to happen? I drifted naturally into buying whatever I wanted, and asking for change. Within a week I was sumptuously equipped with all needful comforts and luxuries, and was housed in an expensive private hotel in Hanover Square. I took my dinners there, but for breakfast I stuck by Harris's humble feeding-house, where I had got my first meal on my million-pound bill. I was the making of Harris. The fact had gone all abroad that the foreign crank who carried million-pound bills in his vest pocket was the patron saint of the place. That was enough. From being a poor, struggling, little hand-to-mouth enterprise, it had become celebrated, and overcrowded with customers. Harris was so grateful that he forced loans upon me, and would not be denied; and so, pauper as I was, I had money to spend, and was living like the rich and the great. I judged that there was going to be a crash by and by, but I was in now and must swim across or drown. You see there was just that element of impending disaster to give a serious side, a sober side, yes, a tragic side, to a state of things which would otherwise have been purely ridiculous. In the night, in the dark, the tragedy part was always to the front, and always warning, always threatening; and so I moaned and tossed, and sleep was hard to find. But in the cheerful daylight the tragedy element faded out and disappeared, and I walked on air, and was happy to giddiness, to intoxication, you may say.

And it was natural; for I had become one of the notorieties of the metropolis of the world, and it turned my head, not just a little, but a good deal. You could not take up a newspaper, English, Scotch, or Irish, without finding in it one or more references to the 'vest-pocket million-pounder' and his latest doings and sayings. At first, in these mentions, I was at the bottom of the personal-gossip column; next, I was listed above the knights, next above the baronets, next above the barons, and so on, and so on, climbing steadily, as my notoriety augmented, until I reached the highest altitude possible, and there I remained, taking precedence of all dukes not royal, and of all ecclesiastics except the primate of all England. But mind, this was not fame; as yet I had achieved only notoriety. Then came the climaxing stroke – the accolade, so to speak – which in a single instant transmuted the perishable dross of notoriety into the enduring gold of fame: *Punch* caricatured me! Yes, I was a made man now; my place was established. I might be joked about still, but reverently, not hilariously, not rudely; I could be smiled at, but not laughed at. The time for that had gone by. *Punch* pictured me all a-flutter with rags, dickering with a beefeater for the Tower of London. Well, you can imagine how it was with a young fellow who had never been taken notice of before, and now all of a sudden couldn't say a thing that wasn't taken up and repeated everywhere; couldn't stir abroad without constantly overhearing the remark flying from lip to lip, 'There he goes; that's him!'; couldn't take his breakfast without a crowd to look on; couldn't appear in an opera-box without concentrating there the fire of a thousand lorgnettes. Why, I just swam in glory all day long – that is the amount of it.

You know, I even kept my old suit of rags, and every now and then appeared in them, so as to have the old pleasure of buying trifles, and being insulted, and then shooting the scoffer dead with the million-pound bill. But I couldn't keep that up. The illustrated papers made the outfit so familiar that when I went out in it I was at once recognized and followed by a crowd, and if I attempted a purchase the man would offer me his whole shop on credit before I could pull my note on him.

About the tenth day of my fame I went to fulfill my duty to my flag by paying my respects to the American minister. He received me with the enthusiasm proper in my case, upbraided me for being so tardy in my duty, and said that there was only one way to get his forgiveness, and that was to take the seat at his dinner-party that night made vacant by the illness of one of his guests. I said I would, and we got to talking. It turned out that he and my father had been schoolmates in boyhood, Yale students together later, and always warm friends up to my father's death. So then he required me to put in at his house all the odd time I might have to spare, and I was very willing, of course.

In fact, I was more than willing; I was glad. When the crash should come, he might somehow be able to save me from total destruction; I didn't know how, but he might think of a way, maybe. I couldn't venture to unbosom myself to him at this late date, a thing which I would have been quick to do in the beginning of this awful career of mine in London. No, I couldn't venture it now; I was in too deep; that is, too deep for me to be risking revelations to so new a friend, though not clear beyond my depth, as I looked at it. Because, you see, with all my borrowing, I was carefully keeping within my means – I mean within my salary. Of course, I couldn't *know* what my salary was going to be, but I had a good enough basis for an estimate in the fact that if I won the bet I was to have *choice* of any situation in that rich old gentleman's gift provided I was competent – and I should certainly prove competent; I hadn't any doubt about that. And as to the bet, I wasn't worrying about that; I had always been lucky. Now my estimate of the salary was six hundred to a thousand a year; say, six hundred for the first year, and so on up year by year, till I struck the upper figure by proved merit. At present I was only in debt for my first year's salary. Everybody had been trying to lend me money, but I had fought off the most of them on one pretext or another; so this indebtedness represented only £300 borrowed money, the other £300 represented my keep and my purchases. I believed my second year's salary would carry me through the rest of the month if I went on being cautious and economical, and I intended to look sharply out for that. My month ended, my employer back from his journey, I should be all right once more, for I should at once divide the two years' salary among my creditors by assignment, and get right down to my work.

It was a lovely dinner-party of fourteen. The Duke and Duchess of Shoreditch, and their daughter the Lady Anne-Grace-Eleanor-Celeste-and-so-forth-and-so-forth-de-Bohun, the Earl and Countess of Newgate, Viscount Cheapside, Lord and Lady Blatherskite, some untitled people of both sexes, the minister and his wife and daughter, and his daughter's visiting friend, an English girl of twenty-two, named Portia Langham, whom I fell in love with in two minutes, and she with me – I could see it without glasses. There was still another guest, an American – but I am a little ahead of my story. While the people were still in the drawing-room, whetting up for dinner, and coldly inspecting the latecomers, the servant announced:

'Mr Lloyd Hastings.'

The moment the usual civilities were over, Hastings caught sight of me, and came straight with cordially outstretched hand; then stopped short when about to shake, and said, with an embarrassed look:

'I beg your pardon, sir, I thought I knew you.'

'Why, you do know me, old fellow.'

'No. Are *you* the – the—'

'Vest-pocket monster? I am, indeed. Don't be afraid to call me by my nickname; I'm used to it.'

'Well, well, well, this is a surprise. Once or twice I've seen your own name coupled with the nickname, but it never occurred to me that *you* could be the Henry Adams referred to. Why, it isn't six months since you were clerking away for Blake

Hopkins in Frisco on a salary, and sitting up nights on an extra allowance, helping me arrange and verify the Gould and Curry Extension papers and statistics. The idea of your being in London, and a vast millionaire, and a colossal celebrity! Why, it's the Arabian Nights come again. Man, I can't take it in at all; can't realize it; give me time to settle the whirl in my head.'

'The fact is, Lloyd, you are no worse off than I am. I can't realize it myself.'

'Dear me, it *is* stunning, now isn't it? Why, it's just three months today since we went to the Miners' restaurant—'

'No; the What Cheer.'

'Right, it *was* the What Cheer; went there at two in the morning, and had a chop and coffee after a hard six-hours grind over those Extension papers, and I tried to persuade you to come to London with me, and offered to get leave of absence for you and pay all your expenses, and give you something over if I succeeded in making the sale; and you would not listen to me, said I wouldn't succeed, and you couldn't afford to lose the run of business and be no end of time getting the hang of things again when you got back home. And yet here you are. How odd it all is! How did you happen to come, and whatever *did* give you this incredible start?'

'Oh, just an accident. It's a long story – a romance, a body may say. I'll tell you all about it, but not now.'

'When?'

'The end of this month.'

'That's more than a fortnight yet. It's too much of a strain on a person's curiosity. Make it a week.'

'I can't. You'll know why, by and by. But how's the trade getting along?'

His cheerfulness vanished like a breath, and he said with a sigh:

'You were a true prophet, Hal, a true prophet. I wish I hadn't come. I don't want to talk about it.'

'But you must. You must come and stop with me tonight, when we leave here, and tell me all about it.'

'Oh, may I? Are you in earnest?' and the water showed in his eyes.

'Yes; I want to hear the whole story, every word.'

'I'm so grateful! Just to find a human interest once more, in some voice and in some eye, in me and affairs of mine, after what I've been through here – lord! I could go down on my knees for it!'

He gripped my hand hard, and braced up, and was all right and lively after that for the dinner – which didn't come off. No; the usual thing happened, the thing that is always happening under that vicious and aggravating English system – the matter of precedence couldn't be settled, and so there was no dinner. Englishmen always eat dinner before they go out to dinner, because *they* know the risks they are running; but nobody ever warns the stranger, and so he walks placidly into the trap. Of course, nobody was hurt this time, because we had all been to dinner, none of us being novices excepting Hastings, and he having been informed by the minister at the time that he invited him that in deference to the English custom he had not provided any dinner. Everybody took a lady and processioned down to the dining-room because it is usual to go through the motions; but there the dispute began. The Duke of Shoreditch wanted to take precedence, and sit at the head of the table, holding that he out-ranked a minister who represented merely a nation and not a monarch; but I stood for my rights, and refused to yield. In the gossip column I ranked all dukes not royal, and said so, and claimed precedence of this one. It couldn't be settled, of course, struggle as we might and did, he finally (and injudiciously) trying to play birth and antiquity, and I 'seeing' his Conqueror and 'raising' him with Adam, whose direct posterity I was, as shown by my name, while *he* was of a collateral branch, as shown by *his*, and by his recent Norman origin; so we all processioned back to the drawing-room again and had a perpendicular lunch – plate of sardines and a strawberry, and you group yourself and stand up and eat it. Here the religion of precedence is not so strenuous; the two persons of highest rank chuck up a shilling, the one that wins has first go at his strawberry, and the loser gets the shilling. The next two chuck up, then the next two, and so on. After refreshment, tables were brought, and we all played cribbage, sixpence a game. The English never play any game for amuse-ment. If they can't make something or lose something – they don't care which – they won't play.

We had a lovely time; certainly two of us had, Miss Langham and I. I was so bewitched with her that I couldn't count my hands if they went above a double sequence; and when I struck home I never discovered it, and started up the outside row again, and would have lost the game every time, only the girl did the same, she being in just my condition, you see; and consequently neither of us ever got out, or cared to wonder why we didn't; we only just knew we were happy, and didn't wish to know anything else, and didn't want to be interrupted. And I *told* her – I did, indeed – told her I loved her; and she – well, she blushed till her hair turned red, but she liked it; she *said* she did. Oh, there was never such an evening! Every time I pegged I put on a postscript; every time she pegged she acknowledged receipt of it, counting the hands the same. Why, I couldn't even say 'Two for his heels' without adding 'My, how sweet you do look!' and she would say, 'Fifteen two, fifteen four, fifteen six, and a pair are eight, and eight are sixteen – *do* you think so?' – peeping out aslant from under her lashes, you know, so sweet and cunning. Oh, it was just *too-too*!

Well, I was perfectly honest and square with her; told her I hadn't a cent in the world but just the million-pound note she'd heard so much talk about, and *it* didn't belong to me, and that started her curiosity; and then I talked low, and told her the whole history right from the start, and it nearly killed her laughing. What in the nation she could find to laugh about I couldn't see, but there it was; every half-minute some new detail would fetch her, and I would have to stop as much as a minute and a half to give her a chance to settle down again. Why, she laughed herself lame – she did, indeed; I never saw anything like it. I mean I never saw a painful story – a story of a person's troubles and worries and fears – produce just *that* kind of effect before. So I loved her all the more, seeing she could be so cheerful when there wasn't anything to be cheerful about; for I might soon need that kind of wife, you know, the way things looked. Of course, I told her we should have to wait a couple of years, till I could catch up on my salary; but she didn't mind that, only she hoped I would be as careful as possible in the matter of expenses, and not let them run the least risk of trenching on our third year's pay. Then she began to get a little worried, and wondered if we were making any mistake, and starting the salary on a higher figure for the first year than I would get. This was good sense, and it made me feel a little less confident than I had been feeling before; but it gave me a good business idea, and I brought it frankly out.

'Portia, dear, would you mind going with me that day, when I confront those old gentlemen?'

She shrank a little, but said:

'N-o; if my being with you would help hearten you. But – would it be quite proper, do you think?'

'No, I don't know that it would – in fact, I'm afraid it wouldn't; but, you see, there's so *much* dependent upon it that—'

'Then I'll go anyway, proper or improper,' she said, with a beautiful and generous enthusiasm. 'Oh, I shall be so happy to think I'm helping!'

'Helping, dear? Why, you'll be doing it all. You're so beautiful and so lovely and so winning, that with you there I can pile our salary up till I break those good old fellows, and they'll never have the heart to struggle.'

Sho! you should have seen the rich blood mount, and her happy eyes shine!

'You wicked flatterer! There isn't a word of truth in what you say, but still I'll go with you. Maybe it will teach you not to expect other people to look with your eyes.'

Were my doubts dissipated? Was my confidence restored? You may judge by this fact: privately I raised my salary to twelve hundred the first year on the spot. But I didn't tell her: I saved it for a surprise.

All the way home I was in the clouds, Hastings talking, I not hearing a word. When he and I entered my parlor, he brought me to myself with his fervent appreciations of my manifold comforts and luxuries.

'Let me just stand here a little and look my fill. Dear me! it's a palace – it's just a palace! And in it everything a body *could* desire, including cozy coal fire and supper standing ready. Henry, it doesn't merely make me realize how rich you are; it makes me realize, to the bone, to the marrow, how poor I am – how poor I am, and how miserable, how defeated, routed, annihilated!'

Plague take it! this language gave me the cold shudders. It scared me broad awake, and made me comprehend that I was standing on a half-inch crust, with a crater underneath. *I* didn't know I had been dreaming – that is, I hadn't been allowing myself to know it for a while back; but *now* – oh, dear! Deep in debt, not a cent in the world, a lovely girl's happiness or woe in my hands, and nothing in front of me but a salary which might never – oh, *would* never – materialize! Oh, oh, oh! I am ruined past hope! nothing can save me!

'Henry, the mere unconsidered drippings of your daily income would—'

'Oh, my daily income! Here, down with this hot Scotch, and cheer up your soul. Here's with you! Or, no – you're hungry; sit down and—'

'Not a bite for me; I'm past it. I can't eat, these days; but I'll drink with you till I drop. Come!'

'Barrel for barrel, I'm with you! Ready? Here we go! Now, then, Lloyd, unreel your story while I brew.'

'Unreel it? What, again?'

'Again? What do you mean by that?'

'Why, I mean do you want to hear it *over* again?'

'Do I want to hear it *over* again? This *is* a puzzler. Wait; don't take any more of that liquid. You don't need it.'

'Look here, Henry, you alarm me. Didn't I tell you the whole story on the way here?'

'You?'

'Yes, I.'

'I'll be hanged if I heard a word of it.'

'Henry, this is a serious thing. It troubles me. What did you take up yonder at the minister's?'

Then it all flashed on me, and I owned up like a man.

'I took the dearest girl in this world – prisoner!'

So then he came with a rush, and we shook, and shook, and shook till our hands ached; and he didn't blame me for not having heard a word of a story which had lasted while we walked three miles. He just sat down then, like the patient, good fellow he was, and told it all over again. Synopsized, it amounted to this: He had come to England with what he thought was a grand opportunity; he had an 'option' to sell the Gould and Curry Extension for the 'locators' of it, and keep all he could get over a million dollars. He had worked hard, had pulled every wire he knew of, had left no honest expedient untried, had spent nearly all the money he had in the world, had not been able to get a solitary capitalist to listen to him, and his option would run out at the end of the month. In a word, he was ruined. Then he jumped up and cried out:

'Henry, you can save me! You can save me, and you're the only man in the universe that can. Will you do it? *Won't* you do it?'

'Tell me how. Speak out, my boy.'

'Give me a million and my passage home for my "option"! Don't, *don't* refuse!'

I was in a kind of agony. I was right on the point of coming out with the words, 'Lloyd, I'm a pauper myself – absolutely penniless, and in *debt*.' But a white-hot idea came flaming through my head, and I gripped my jaws together, and calmed myself down till I was as cold as a capitalist. Then I said, in a commercial and self-possessed way:

'I will save you, Lloyd—'

'Then I'm already saved! God be merciful to you forever! If ever I—'

'Let me finish, Lloyd. I will save you, but not in that way; for that would not be fair to you, after your hard work, and the risks you've run. I don't need to buy mines; I can keep my capital moving, in a commercial center like London, without that; it's what I'm at, all the time; but here is what I'll do. I know all about that mine, of course; I know its immense value, and can swear to it if anybody wishes it. You shall sell out inside of the fortnight for three millions cash, using my name freely, and we'll divide, share and share alike.'

Do you know, he would have danced the furniture to kindling-wood in his insane joy, and broken everything on the place, if I hadn't tripped him up and tied him.

Then he lay there, perfectly happy, saying:

'I may use your name! Your name – think of it! Man, they'll flock in droves, these rich Londoners; they'll *fight* for that stock! I'm a made man, I'm a made man forever, and I'll never forget you as long as I live!'

In less than twenty-four hours London was abuzz! I hadn't anything to do, day after day, but sit at home, and say to all comers:

'Yes; I told him to refer to me. I know the man, and I know

the mine. His character is above reproach, and the mine is worth far more than he asks for it.'

Meantime I spent all my evenings at the minister's with Portia. I didn't say a word to her about the mine; I saved it for a surprise. We talked salary; never anything but salary and love; sometimes love, sometimes salary, sometimes love and salary together. And my! the interest the minister's wife and daughter took in our little affair, and the endless ingenuities they invented to save us from interruption, and to keep the minister in the dark and unsuspicious – well, it was just lovely of them!

When the month was up at last, I had a million dollars to my credit in the London and County Bank, and Hastings was fixed in the same way. Dressed at my level best, I drove by the house in Portland Place, judged by the look of things that my birds were home again, went on toward the minister's and got my precious, and we started back, talking salary with all our might. She was so excited and anxious that it made her just intolerably beautiful. I said:

'Dearie, the way you're looking it's a crime to strike for a salary a single penny under three thousand a year.'

'Henry, Henry, you'll ruin us!'

'Don't you be afraid. Just keep up those looks and trust to me. It'll all come out right.'

So, as it turned out, I had to keep bolstering up *her* courage all the way. She kept pleading with me, and saying:

'Oh, please remember that if we ask for too much we may get no salary at all; and then what will become of us, with no way in the world to earn our living?'

We were ushered in by that same servant, and there they were, the two old gentlemen. Of course, they were surprised to see that wonderful creature with me, but I said:

'It's all right, gentlemen; she is my future stay and helpmate.'

And I introduced them to her, and called them by name. It didn't surprise them; they knew I would know enough to consult the directory. They seated us, and were very polite to me, and very solicitous to relieve her from embarrassment, and put her as much at her ease as they could. Then I said:

'Gentlemen, I am ready to report.'

'We are glad to hear it,' said *my* man, 'for now we can decide the bet which my brother Abel and I made. If you have won for me, you shall have any situation in my gift. Have you the million-pound note?'

'Here it is, sir,' and I handed it to him.

'I've won!' he shouted, and slapped Abel on the back. '*Now* what do you say, brother?'

'I say he *did* survive, and I've lost twenty thousand pounds. I never would have believed it.'

'I've a further report to make,' I said, 'and a pretty long one. I want you to let me come soon, and detail my whole month's history; and I promise you it's worth hearing. Meantime, take a look at that.'

'What, man! Certificate of deposit for £200,000. Is it yours?'

'Mine. I earned it by thirty days' judicious use of that little loan you let me have. And the only use I made of it was to buy trifles and offer the bill in change.'

'Come, this is astonishing! It's incredible, man!'

'Never mind, I'll prove it. Don't take my word unsupported.'

But now Portia's turn was come to be surprised. Her eyes were spread wide, and she said:

'Henry, is that really your money? Have you been fibbing to me?'

'I have, indeed, dearie. But you'll forgive me, *I* know.'

She put up an arch pout, and said:

'Don't you be so sure. You are a naughty thing to deceive me so!'

'Oh, you'll get over it, sweetheart, you'll get over it; it was only fun, you know. Come, let's be going.'

'But wait, wait! The situation, you know. I want to give you the situation,' said my man.

'Well,' I said, 'I'm just as grateful as I can be, but really I don't want one.'

'But you can have the very choicest one in my gift.'

'Thanks again, with all my heart; but I don't even want *that* one.'

'Henry, I'm ashamed of you. You don't half thank the good gentleman. May I do it for you?'

'Indeed, you shall, dear, if you can improve it. Let us see you try.'

She walked to my man, got up in his lap, put her arm round his neck, and kissed him right on the mouth. Then the two old gentlemen shouted with laughter, but I was dumfounded, just petrified, as you may say. Portia said:

'Papa, he has said you haven't a situation in your gift that he'd take; and I feel just as hurt as—'

'My darling, is that your papa?'

'Yes; he's my step-papa, and the dearest one that ever was. You understand now, don't you, why I was able to laugh when you told me at the minister's, not knowing my relationships, what trouble and worry Papa's and Uncle Abel's scheme was giving you?'

Of course, I spoke right up now, without any fooling, and went straight to the point.

'Oh, my dearest dear sir, I want to take back what I said. You *have* got a situation open that I want.'

'Name it.'

'Son-in-law.'

'Well, well, well! But you know, if you haven't ever served in that capacity, you, of course, can't furnish recommendations of a sort to satisfy the conditions of the contract, and so—'

'Try me – oh, do, I beg of you! Only just try me thirty or forty years, and if—'

'Oh, well, all right; it's but a little thing to ask, take her along.'

Happy, we two? There are not words enough in the unabridged to describe it. And when London got the whole history, a day or two later, of my month's adventures with that banknote, and how they ended, did London talk, and have a good time? Yes.

My Portia's papa took that friendly and hospitable bill back to the Bank of England and cashed it; then the Bank canceled it and made him a present of it, and he gave it to us at our wedding, and it has always hung in its frame in the sacredest place in our home ever since. For it gave me my Portia. But for it I could not have remained in London, would not have appeared at the minister's, never should have met her. And so I always say, 'Yes, it's a million-pounder, as you see; but it never made but one purchase in its life, and *then* got the article for only about a tenth part of its value.'

An Item Which the Editor Himself Could Not Understand

Our esteemed friend, Mr John William Skae, of Virginia City, walked into the office where we are sub-editor at a late hour last night, with an expression of profound and heartfelt suffering upon his countenance, and, sighing heavily, laid the following item reverently upon the desk, and walked slowly out again. He paused a moment at the door, and seemed struggling to command his feelings sufficiently to enable him to speak, and then, nodding his head toward his manuscript, ejaculated in a broken voice, 'Friend of mine – oh! how sad!' and burst into tears. We were so moved at his distress that we did not think to call him back and endeavor to comfort him until he was gone and it was too late. The paper had already gone to press, but knowing that our friend would consider the publication of this item important, and cherishing the hope that to print it would afford a melancholy satisfaction to his sorrowing heart, we stopped the press at once and inserted it in our columns:

DISTRESSING ACCIDENT

Last evening about 6 o'clock, as Mr William Schuyler, an old and respectable citizen of South Park, was leaving his residence to go downtown, as has been his usual custom for many years, with the exception only of a short interval in the spring of 1850, during which he was confined to his bed by injuries received in attempting to stop a runaway horse by thoughtlessly placing himself directly in its wake and throwing up his hands and shouting, which, if he had done so even a single moment sooner, must inevitably have frightened the animal still more instead of checking its speed, although disastrous enough to himself as it was, and rendered more melancholy and distressing by reason of the presence of his wife's mother, who was there and saw the sad occurrence, notwithstanding it is at least likely, though not necessarily so, that she should be reconnoitering in another direction when incidents occur, not being vivacious and on the lookout, as a general thing, but even the reverse, as her own mother is said to have stated, who is no more, but died in the full hope of a glorious resurrection, upwards of three years ago, aged 86, being a Christian woman and without guile, as it were, or property, in consequence of the fire of 1849, which destroyed every blasted thing she had in the world. But such is life. Let us all take warning by this solemn occurrence, and let us endeavor so to conduct ourselves that when we come to die we can do it. Let us place our hands upon our hearts, and say with earnestness and sincerity that from this day forth we will beware of the intoxicating bowl.

First Edition of the Californian

The boss-editor has been in here raising the very mischief, and tearing his hair and kicking the furniture about, and abusing me like a pickpocket. He says that every time he leaves me in charge of the paper for half an hour, I get imposed upon by the first infant or the first idiot that comes along. And he says that distressing item of Johnny Skae's is nothing but a lot of distressing bosh, and has got no point to it and no sense in it and no information in it, and that there was no earthly necessity for stopping the press to publish it. He says every man he meets has insinuated that somebody about the *Californian* office has gone crazy.

Now all this comes of being good-hearted. If I had been as unaccommodating and unsympathetic as some people, I would have told Johnny Skae that I wouldn't receive his communication at such a late hour, and to go to blazes with it; but no, his snuffling distress touched my heart, and I jumped at the chance of doing something to modify his misery. I never read his item to see whether there was anything wrong about it, but hastily wrote the few lines which preceded it, and sent it to the printers. And what has my kindness done for me? It has done nothing but bring down upon me a storm of abuse and ornamental blasphemy.

Now, I will just read that item myself, and see if there is any foundation for all this fuss. And if there is, the author of it shall hear from me.

I have read it, and I am bound to admit that it seems a little mixed at a first glance. However, I will peruse it once more.

I have read it again, and it does really seem a good deal more mixed than ever.

I have read it over five times, but if I can get at the meaning of it, I wish I may get my just deserts. It won't bear analysis. There are things about it which I can not understand at all. It don't say whatever became of William Schuyler. It just says enough about him to get one interested in his career, and then drops him. Who is William Schuyler, anyhow, and what part of South Park did he live in, and if he started downtown at six o'clock, did he ever get there, and if he did, did anything happen to him? Is *he* the individual that met with the 'distressing accident'? Considering the elaborate circumstantiality of detail observable in the item, it seems to me that it ought to contain more information than it does. On the contrary, it is obscure – and not only obscure, but utterly incomprehensible. Was the breaking of Mr Schuyler's leg, fifteen years ago, the 'distressing accident' that plunged Mr Skae into unspeakable grief, and caused him to come up here at dead of night and stop our press to acquaint the world with the unfortunate circumstance? Or did the 'distressing accident' consist in the destruction of Schuyler's mother-in-law's property in early times? Or did it consist in the death of that person herself three years ago? (Albeit it does not appear that she died by accident.) In a word, what *did* that 'distressing accident' consist in? What did that driveling ass of a Schuyler stand *in the wake* of a runaway horse for, with his shouting and gesticulating, if he wanted to stop him? And how the mischief could he get run over by a horse that had already passed beyond him? And what are we to 'take warning' by? and how is this extraordinary chapter of incomprehensibilities going to be a 'lesson' to us? And above all, what has the 'intoxicating bowl' got to do with it, anyhow? It is not stated that Schuyler drank, or that his wife drank, or that his mother-in-law drank, or that the horse drank – wherefore, then, the reference to the intoxicating bowl? It does seem to me that, if Mr Skae had let the intoxicating bowl alone himself, he never would have got into so much trouble about this infernal imaginary distressing accident. I have read his absurd item over and over again, with all its insinuating plausibility, until my head swims; but I can make neither head nor tail of it. There certainly seems to have been an accident of some kind or other, but it is impossible to determine what the nature of it was, or who was the sufferer by it. I do not like to do it, but I feel compelled to request that the next time anything happens to one of Mr Skae's friends, he will append such explanatory notes to his account of it as will enable me to find out what sort of an accident it was and whom it happened to. I had rather all his friends should die than that I should be driven to the verge of lunacy again in trying to cipher out the meaning of another such production as the above.

The Great Earthquake in San Francisco

San Francisco, Oct. 8, 1865

EDITOR'S REVIEW.

Long before this reaches your city, the telegraph will have
mentioned to you, casually, that San Francisco was visited by an
earthquake today, and the daily prints will have conveyed the
news to their readers with the same air of indifference with
which it was clothed by the unimpassioned lightning, and five
minutes afterward the world will have forgotten the circumstance, under the impression that just such earthquakes are
everyday occurrences here, and therefore not worth remembering. But if you had been here you would have conceived very
different notions from these. Today's earthquake was no ordinary affair. It is likely that future earthquakes in this vicinity, for
years to come, will suffer by comparison with it.

I have tried a good many of them here, and of several varieties – some that came in the form of a universal shiver; others
that gave us two or three sudden upward heaves from below;
others that swayed grandly and deliberately from side to side;
and still others that came rolling and undulating beneath our
feet like a great wave of the sea. But today's specimen belonged
to a new, and, I hope, a very rare, breed of earthquakes. First,
there was a quick, heavy shock; three or four seconds elap-
sed, and then the city and county of San Francisco darted violently from north-west to south-east, and from south-east to
north-west five times with extraordinary energy and rapidity. I
say 'darted', because that word comes nearest to describing the
movement.

I was walking along Third street, and facing north, when the
first shock came; I was walking fast, and it 'broke up my gait'
pretty completely – checked me – just as a strong wind will do
when you turn a corner and face it suddenly. That shock was
coming from the north-west, and I met it halfway. I took about six
or seven steps (went back and measured the distance afterwards

to decide a bet about the interval of time between the first and second shocks), and was just turning the corner into Howard street when those five angry 'darts' came. I suppose the first of them proceeded from the south-east, because it moved my feet toward the opposite point of the compass – to the left – and made me stagger against the corner house on my right. The noise accompanying the shocks was a tremendous rasping sound, like the violent shaking and grinding together of a block of brick houses. It was about the most disagreeable sound you can imagine.

I will set it down here as a maxim that the operations of the human intellect are much accelerated by an earthquake. Usually I do not think rapidly – but I did upon this occasion. I thought rapidly, vividly, and distinctly. With the first shock of the five, I thought – 'I recognize that motion – this is an earthquake.' With the second, I thought, 'What a luxury this will be for the morning papers.' With the third shock, I thought, 'Well, my boy, you had better be getting out of this.' Each of these thoughts was only the hundredth part of a second in passing through my mind. There is no incentive to rapid reasoning like an earthquake. I then sidled out toward the middle of the street – and I may say that I sidled out with some degree of activity, too. There is nothing like an earthquake to hurry a man up when he starts to go anywhere. As I went I glanced down to my left and saw the whole front of a large four-story brick building spew out and 'splatter' abroad over the street in front of it. Another thought steamed through my brain. I thought this was going to be the greatest earthquake of the century, and that the city was going to be destroyed entirely, and I took out my watch and timed the event. It was twelve minutes to one o'clock, p.m. This showed great coolness and presence of mind on my part – most people would have been hunting for something to climb, instead of looking out for the best interests of history.

As I walked down the street – down the middle of the street – frequently glancing up with a sagacious eye at the houses on either side to see which way they were going to fall, I felt the earth shivering gently under me, and grew moderately sea-sick (and remained so for nearly an hour; others became excessively sleepy as well as sea-sick, and were obliged to go to bed, and refresh themselves with a sound nap). A minute before the earthquake I had three or four streets pretty much to myself, as far as I could see down them (for we are a Sunday-respecting community, and go out of town to break the Sabbath) but five seconds after it I was lost in a swarm of crying children, and coatless, hatless men and shrieking women. They were all in motion, too, and no two of them trying to run in the same direction. They charged simultaneously from opposite rows of houses, like opposing regiments from ambuscades, and came together with a crash and a yell in the centre of the street. Then came chaos and confusion, and a general digging out for somewhere else, they didn't know where, and didn't care.

Everything that *was* done, was done in the twinkling of an eye – there was no apathy visible anywhere. A street car stopped close at hand, and disgorged its passengers so suddenly that they all seemed to flash out at the self-same instant of time.

The crowd was in danger from outside influences for a while. A horse was coming down Third street, with a buggy attached to him, and following after him – either by accident or design – and the horse was either frightened at the earthquake or a good deal surprised – I cannot say which, because I do not know how horses are usually affected by such things – but at any rate he must have been opposed to earthquakes, because he started to leave there, and took the buggy and his master with him, and scattered them over a piece of ground as large as an ordinary park, and finally fetched up against a lamp-post with nothing hanging to him but a few strips of harness suitable for fiddlestrings. However he might have been affected previously, the expression upon his countenance at this time was one of unqualified surprise. The driver of the buggy was found intact and unhurt, but to the last degree dusty and blasphemous. As the crowds along the street had fortunately taken chances on the earthquake and opened out to let the horse pass, no one was injured by his stampede.

When I got to the locality of the shipwrecked four-story building before spoken of, I found that the front of it, from eaves to pavement, had fallen out, and lay in ruins on the ground. The roof and floors were broken down and dilapidated. It was a new structure and unoccupied, and by rare good luck it damaged itself alone by its fall. The walls were only three bricks thick, a fact which, taking into account the earthquakiness of the country, evinces an unquestioning trust in Providence, on the part of the proprietor, which is as gratifying as it is impolitic and reckless.

I turned into Mission street and walked down to Second without finding any evidences of the great ague, but in Second street itself I traveled half a block on shattered window glass. The large hotels, further downtown, were all standing, but the boarders were all in the street. The plastering had fallen in many of the rooms, and a gentleman who was in an attic chamber of the Cosmopolitan at the time of the quake, told me the water 'sloshed' out of the great tanks on the roof, and fell in sheets of spray to the court below. He said the huge building rocked like a cradle after the first grand spasms; the walls seemed to 'belly' inward like a sail, and flakes of plastering began to drop on him. He then went out and slid, feet foremost, down one or two hundred feet of banisters – partly for amusement, but chiefly with an eye to expedition. He said he flashed by the frantic crowds in each succeeding story like a telegraphic despatch.

Several ladies felt a faintness and dizziness in the head, and one, (incredible as it may seem) weighing over two hundred and fifty pounds, fainted all over. They hauled her out of her room, and deluged her with water, but for nearly half an hour all efforts to resuscitate her were fruitless. It is said that the noise of the earthquake on the ground floor of the hotel, which is paved with marble, was as if forty freight trains were thundering over it. The large billiard saloon in the rear of the office was full of people at the time, but a moment afterward numbers of them were seen flying up the street with their billiard-cues in their hands, like a squad of routed lancers. Three jumped out of a back window into the central court, and found themselves imprisoned – for the tall, spike-armed iron gate which bars the passageway for coal and provision wagons was locked.

'What did you do then?' I asked.

'Well, Conrad, from Humboldt – you know him – Conrad said, "Let's climb over, boys, and be devilish quick about it, too" – and he made a dash for it – but Smith and me started in last and were first over – because the seat of Conrad's pants caught on the spikes at the top, and we left him hanging there and yelling like an Injun.'

And then my friend called my attention to the gate and said: 'There's the gate – ten foot high, I should think, and nothing to catch hold of to climb by – but don't you know I went over that gate like a shot out of a shovel, and took my billiard-cue along with me? I did it, as certain as I am standing here – but if I could do it again for fifteen hundred thousand dollars, I'll be d—d – not unless there was another earthquake, anyway.'

From the fashionable barber-shops in the vicinity gentlemen rushed into the thronged streets in their shirt-sleeves, with towels round their necks, and with one side of their faces smoothly shaved, and the other side foamy with lather.

One gentleman was having his corns cut by a barber, when the premonitory shock came. The barber's under-jaw dropped, and he stared aghast at the dancing furniture. The gentleman winked complacently at the bystanders, and said with fine humor, 'Oh, go on with your surgery, John – it's nothing but an earthquake, no use to run, you know, because if you're going to the devil anyhow, you might as well start from here as outside.' Just then the earth commenced its hideous grinding and surging movement, and the gentleman retreated toward the door, remarking, 'However, John, if we've *got* to go, perhaps we'd as well start from the street, after all.'

On North Beach, men ran out of the bathing houses attired like the Greek slave, and mingled desperately with ladies and gentlemen who were as badly frightened as themselves, but more elaborately dressed.

The City Hall, which is a large building, was so dismembered, and its walls sprung apart from each other, that the structure will doubtless have to be pulled down. The earthquake rang a merry peal on the City Hall bell, the 'clapper' of which weighs seventy-eight pounds. It is said that several engine companies turned out, under the impression that the alarm was struck by the fire-telegraph.

Bells of all sorts and sizes were rung by the shake throughout the city, and from what I can learn the earthquake formally announced its visit on every door-bell in town. One gentleman said: 'My door-bell fell to ringing violently, but I said to myself, "I know you – you are an Earthquake; and you appear to be in a hurry; but you'll jingle that bell considerably before I let you in –

on the contrary, I'll crawl under this sofa and get out of the way of the plastering."'

I went down toward the city front and found a brick warehouse mashed in as if some foreigner from Brobdignag had sat down on it.

All down Battery street the large brick wholesale houses were pretty universally shaken up, and some of them badly damaged, the roof of one being crushed in, and the fire-walls of one or two being ripped off even with the tops of the upper windows, and dumped into the street below.

The tall shot tower in First street weathered the storm, but persons who watched it respectfully from a distance said it swayed to and fro like a drunken giant.

I saw three chimneys which were broken in two about three feet from the top, and the upper sections slewed around until they sat corner-wise on the lower ones.

The damage done to houses by this earthquake is estimated at over half a million of dollars.

But I had rather talk about the 'incidents'. The Rev. Mr Harmon, Principal of the Pacific Female Seminary, at Oakland, just across the Bay from here, had his entire flock of young ladies at church – and also his wife and children – and was watching and protecting them jealously, like one of those infernal scaly monsters with a pestilential breath that were employed to stand guard over imprisoned heroines in the days of chivalry, and who always proved inefficient in the hour of danger – he was watching them, I say, when the earthquake came, and what do you imagine he did, then? Why that confiding trust in Providence which had sustained him through a long ministerial career all at once deserted him, and he got up and ran like a quarter-horse. But that was not the misfortune of it. The exasperating feature of it was that his wife and children and all the school-girls remained bravely in their seats and sat the earthquake through without flinching. Oakland talks and laughs again at the Pacific Female Seminary.

The Superintendent of the Congregational Sunday School in Oakland had just given out the text, 'And the earth shook and trembled', when the earthquake came along and took up the text and preached the sermon for him.

215

The Pastor of Starr King's church, the Rev. Mr Stebbins, came down out of his pulpit after the first shock and embraced a woman. It was an instance of great presence of mind. Some say the woman was his wife, but I regard the remark as envious and malicious. Upon occasions like this, people who are too much scared to seize upon an offered advantage are always ready to depreciate the superior judgment and sagacity of those who profited by the opportunity they lost themselves.

In a certain aristocratic locality uptown, the wife of a foreign dignitary is the acknowledged leader of fashion, and whenever she emerges from her house all the ladies in the vicinity fly to the windows to see what she has 'got on', so that they may make immediate arrangements to procure similar costumes for themselves. Well, in the midst of the earthquake, the beautiful foreign woman [who had just indulged in a bath] appeared in the street *with a towel around her neck*. It was all the raiment she had on. Consequently, in that vicinity, a towel around the neck is considered the only orthodox 'earthquake costume'. Well, and why not? It is elegant, and airy, and simple, and graceful, and pretty, and are not these the chief requisites in female dress? If it were generally adopted it would go far toward reconciling some people to these dreaded earthquakes.

An enterprising barkeeper downtown who is generally up with the times, has already invented a sensation drink to meet the requirements of our present peculiar circumstances. A friend in whom I have confidence thus describes it to me: 'A tall ale-glass is nearly filled with California brandy and Angelica wine – one part of the former to two of the latter; fill to the brim with champagne; charge the drink with electricity from a powerful galvanic battery, and swallow it before the lightning cools. Then march forth – and before you have gone a hundred yards you will think you are occupying the whole street; a parlor clock will look as big as a church; to blow your nose will astonish you like the explosion of a mine, and the most trivial abstract matter will seem as important as the Day of Judgment. When you want this extraordinary drink, disburse your twenty-five cents, and call for an "EARTHQUAKE".'

Punch, Brothers, Punch

Will the reader please to cast his eye over the following lines, and see if he can discover anything harmful in them?

Conductor, when you receive a fare,
Punch in the presence of the passenjare!
A blue trip slip for an eight-cent fare,
A buff trip slip for a six-cent fare,
A pink trip slip for a three-cent fare,
Punch in the presence of the passenjare!

CHORUS
Punch, brothers! punch with care!
Punch in the presence of the passenjare!

I came across these jingling rhymes in a newspaper, a little while ago, and read them a couple of times. They took instant and entire possession of me. All through breakfast they went waltzing through my brain; and when, at last, I rolled up my napkin, I could not tell whether I had eaten anything or not. I had carefully laid out my day's work the day before – a thrilling tragedy in the novel which I am writing. I went to my den to begin my deed of blood. I took up my pen, but all I could get it to say was, 'Punch in the presence of the passenjare.' I fought hard for an hour, but it was useless. My head kept humming, 'A blue trip slip for an eight-cent fare, a buff trip slip for a six-cent fare,' and so on and so on, without peace or respite. The day's work was ruined – I could see that plainly enough. I gave up and drifted downtown, and presently discovered that my feet were keeping time to that relentless jingle. When I could stand it no longer I altered my step. But it did no good; those rhymes accommodated themselves to the new step and went on harass-ing me just as before. I returned home, and suffered all the afternoon; suffered all through an unconscious and unrefreshing dinner; suffered, and cried, and jingled all through the evening; went to bed and rolled, tossed, and jingled right along, the same as ever; got up at midnight frantic, and tried to read; but there was nothing visible upon the whirling page except 'Punch! punch in the presence of the passenjare.' By sunrise I was out of my mind, and everybody marveled and was distressed at the idiotic burden of my ravings – 'Punch! oh, punch! punch in the presence of the passenjare!'

Two days later, on Saturday morning, I arose, a tottering wreck, and went forth to fulfill an engagement with a valued friend, the Rev. Mr ——, to walk to the Talcott Tower, ten miles distant. He stared at me, but asked no questions. We started. Mr —— talked, talked, talked – as is he wont. I said nothing; I heard nothing. At the end of a mile, Mr —— said:

'Mark, are you sick? I never saw a man look so haggard and worn and absent-minded. Say something, do!'

Drearily, without enthusiasm, I said: 'Punch, brothers, punch with care! Punch in the presence of the passenjare!'

My friend eyed me blankly, looked perplexed, then said:

'I do not think I get your drift, Mark. There does not seem to be any relevancy in what you have said, certainly nothing sad; and yet – maybe it was the way you *said* the words – I never heard anything that sounded so pathetic. What is—'

But I heard no more. I was already far away with my pitiless, heartbreaking 'blue trip slip for an eight-cent fare, buff trip slip for a six-cent fare, pink trip slip for a three-cent fare; punch in the presence of the passenjare'. I do not know what occurred during the other nine miles. However, all of a sudden Mr —— laid his hand on my shoulder and shouted:

'Oh, wake up! wake up! wake up! Don't sleep all day! Here we are at the Tower, man! I have talked myself deaf and dumb and blind, and never got a response. Just look at this magnificent autumn landscape! Look at it! look at it! Feast your eyes on it! You have traveled; you have seen boasted landscapes elsewhere. Come, now, deliver an honest opinion. What do you say to this?'

I sighed wearily, and murmured:

'A buff trip slip for a six-cent fare, a pink trip slip for a three-cent fare, punch in the presence of the passenjare.'

Rev. Mr —— stood there, very grave, full of concern, apparently, and looked long at me; then he said:

'Mark, there is something about this that I cannot understand. Those are about the same words you said before; there does not seem to be anything in them, and yet they nearly break my heart when you say them. Punch in the – how is it they go?'

I began at the beginning and repeated all the lines.

My friend's face lighted with interest. He said:

'Why, what a captivating jingle it is! It is almost music. It flows along so nicely. I have nearly caught the rhymes myself. Say them over just once more, and then I'll have them, sure.'

I said them over. Then Mr —— said them. He made one little mistake, which I corrected. The next time and the next he got them right. Now a great burden seemed to tumble from my shoulders. That torturing jingle departed out of my brain, and a grateful sense of rest and peace descended upon me. I was light-hearted enough to sing; and I did sing for half an hour, straight along, as we went jogging homeward. Then my freed tongue found blessed speech again, and the pent talk of many a weary hour began to gush and flow. It flowed on and on, joyously, jubilantly, until the fountain was empty and dry. As I wrung my friend's hand at parting, I said:

'Haven't we had a royal good time! But now I remember, you haven't said a word for two hours. Come, come, out with something!'

The Rev. Mr —— turned a lack-luster eye upon me, drew a deep sigh, and said, without animation, without apparent consciousness:

'Punch, brothers, punch with care! Punch in the presence of the passenjare!'

A pang shot through me as I said to myself, 'Poor fellow, poor fellow! *he* has got it, now.'

I did not see Mr —— for two or three days after that. Then, on Tuesday evening, he staggered into my presence and sank dejectedly into a seat. He was pale, worn; he was a wreck. He lifted his faded eyes to my face and said:

'Ah, Mark, it was a ruinous investment that I made in those heartless rhymes. They have ridden me like a nightmare, day and night, hour after hour, to this very moment. Since I saw you I have suffered the torments of the lost. Saturday evening I had a sudden call, by telegraph, and took the night train for Boston.

The occasion was the death of a valued old friend who had requested that I should preach his funeral sermon. I took my seat in the cars and set myself to framing the discourse. But I never got beyond the opening paragraph; for then the train started and the car-wheels began their "clack, clack – clack-clack-clack! clack-clack – clack-clack-clack!" and right away those odious rhymes fitted themselves to that accompaniment. For an hour I sat there and set a syllable of those rhymes to every separate and distinct clack the car-wheels made. Why, I was as fagged out, then, as if I had been chopping wood all day. My skull was splitting with headache. It seemed to me that I must go mad if I sat there any longer; so I undressed and went to bed. I stretched myself out in my berth, and – well, you know what the result was. The thing went right along, just the same. "Clack-clack-clack, a blue trip slip, clack-clack-clack, for an eight-cent fare; clack-clack-clack, a buff trip slip, clack-clack-clack, for a six-cent fare, and so on, and so on, and so on – *punch* in the presence of the passenjare!" Sleep? Not a single wink! I was almost a lunatic when I got to Boston. Don't ask me about the funeral. I did the best I could, but every solemn individual sentence was meshed and tangled and woven in and out with "Punch, brothers, punch with care, punch in the presence of the passenjare." And the most distressing thing was that my *delivery* dropped into the undulating rhythm of those pulsing rhymes, and I could actually catch absent-minded people nodding *time* to the swing of it with their stupid heads. And, Mark, you may believe it or not, but before I got through the entire assemblage were placidly bobbing their heads in solemn unison, mourners, undertaker, and all. The moment I had finished, I fled to the anteroom in a state bordering on frenzy. Of course it would be my luck to find a sorrowing and aged maiden aunt of the deceased there, who had arrived from Springfield too late to get into the church. She began to sob, and said:

' "Oh, oh, he is gone, he is gone, and I didn't see him before he died!"

' "Yes!" I said, "he *is* gone, he *is* gone, he *is* gone – oh, *will* this suffering never cease!"

' "You loved him, then! Oh, you too loved him!"

' "Loved him! Loved *who?*"

' "Why, my poor George! my poor nephew!"

' "Oh – *him*! Yes – oh, yes, yes. Certainly – certainly. Punch – punch – oh, this misery will kill me!"

' "Bless you! bless you, sir, for these sweet words! *I*, too, suffer in this dear loss. Were you present during his last moments?"

' "Yes. I – *whose* last moments?"

' "*His*. The dear departed's."

' "Yes! Oh, yes – yes – *yes*! I suppose so, I think so, *I* don't know! Oh, certainly – I was there – *I* was there!"

' "Oh, what a privilege! what a precious privilege! And his last words – oh, tell me, tell me his last words! What did he say?"

' "He said – he said – oh, my head, my head, my head! He said – he said – he never said *any*thing but Punch, punch, *punch* in the presence of the passenjare! Oh, leave me, madam! In the name of all that is generous, leave me to my madness, my misery, my despair! – a buff trip slip for a six-cent fare, a pink trip slip for a three-cent fare – endu-rance *can* no fur-ther go! – PUNCH in the presence of the passenjare!" '

My friend's hopeless eyes rested upon mine a pregnant minute, and then he said impressively:

'Mark, you do not say anything. You do not offer me any hope. But, ah me, it is just as well – it is just as well. You could not do me any good. The time has long gone by when words could comfort me. Something tells me that my tongue is doomed to wag forever to the jigger of that remorseless jingle. There – there it is coming on me again: a blue trip slip for an eight-cent fare, a buff trip slip for a—'

Thus murmuring faint and fainter, my friend sank into a peaceful trance and forgot his sufferings in a blessed respite.

How did I finally save him from an asylum? I took him to a neighboring university and made him discharge the burden of his persecuting rhymes into the eager ears of the poor, unthinking students. How is it with *them*, now? The result is too sad to tell. Why did I write this article? It was for a worthy, even a noble, purpose. It was to warn you, reader, if you should come across those merciless rhymes, to avoid them – avoid them as you would a pestilence!

221

Post-Mortem Poetry

In Philadelphia they have a custom which it would be pleasant to see adopted throughout the land. It is that of appending to published death-notices a little verse or two of comforting poetry. Anyone who is in the habit of reading the daily Philadelphia *Ledger* must frequently be touched by these plaintive tributes to extinguished worth. In Philadelphia, the departure of a child is a circumstance which is not more surely followed by a burial than by the accustomed solacing poesy in the *Public Ledger*. In that city death loses half its terror because the knowledge of its presence comes thus disguised in the sweet drapery of verse. For instance, in a late *Ledger* I find the following (I change the surname):

DIED

HAWKS On the 17th inst., Clara, the daughter of Ephraim and Laura Hawks, aged 21 months and 2 days.

> That merry shout no more I hear,
>   No laughing child I see,
> No little arms are round my neck,
>   No feet upon my knee;
>
> No kisses drop upon my cheek,
>   These lips are sealed to me.
> Dear Lord, how could I give Clara up
>   To any but to Thee?

A child thus mourned could not die wholly discontented. From the *Ledger* of the same date I make the following extract, merely changing the surname, as before:

BECKET On Sunday morning, 19th inst., John P., infant son of George and Julia Becket, aged 1 year, 6 months, and 15 days.

That merry shout no more I hear,
　No laughing child I see,
No little arms are round my neck,
　No feet upon my knee;

No kisses drop upon my cheek,
　These lips are sealed to me.
Dear Lord, how could I give Johnnie up
　To any but to Thee?

The similarity of the emotions as produced in the mourners in these two instances is remarkably evidenced by the singular similarity of thought which they experienced, and the surprising coincidence of language used by them to give it expression.

In the same journal, of the same date, I find the following (surname suppressed, as before):

WAGNER On the 10th inst., Ferguson G., the son of William L. and Martha Theresa Wagner, aged 4 weeks and 1 day.

That merry shout no more I hear,
　No laughing child I see,
No little arms are round my neck,
　No feet upon my knee;

No kisses drop upon my cheek,
　These lips are sealed to me.
Dear Lord, how could I give Ferguson up
　To any but to Thee?

It is strange what power the reiteration of an essentially poetical thought has upon one's feelings. When we take up the *Ledger* and read the poetry about little Clara, we feel an unaccountable depression of the spirits. When we drift further down the column and read the poetry about little Johnnie, the depression of spirits acquires an added emphasis, and we experience tangible suffering. When we saunter along down the column further still and read the poetry about little Ferguson, the word torture but vaguely suggests the anguish that rends us.

In the *Ledger* (same copy referred to above) I find the following (I alter surname, as usual):

WELCH On the 5th inst., Mary C. Welch, wife of William B. Welch, and daughter of Catharine and George W. Markland, in the 29th year of her age.

> A mother dear, a mother kind,
> Has gone and left us all behind.
> Cease to weep, for tears are vain,
> Mother dear is out of pain.
>
> Farewell, husband, children dear,
> Serve thy God with filial fear,
> And meet me in the land above,
> Where all is peace, and joy, and love.

What could be sweeter than that? No collection of salient facts (without reduction to tabular form) could be more succinctly stated than is done in the first stanza by the surviving relatives, and no more concise and comprehensive program of farewells, post-mortuary general orders, etc., could be framed in any form than is done in verse by the deceased in the last stanza. These things insensibly make us wiser and tenderer, and better. Another extract:

BALL On the morning of the 15th inst., Mary E., daughter of John and Sarah F. Ball.

> 'Tis sweet to rest in lively hope
>   That when my change shall come
> Angels will hover round my bed,
>   To waft my spirit home.

The following is apparently the customary form for heads of families:

BURNS On the 20th inst., Michael Burns, aged 40 years.

Dearest father, thou hast left us,
  Here thy loss we deeply feel;
But 'tis God that has bereft us,
  He can all our sorrows heal.

Funeral at 2 o'clock sharp.

There is something very simple and pleasant about the following which, in Philadelphia, seems to be the usual form for consumptives of long standing. (It deplores four distinct cases in the single copy of the *Ledger* which lies on the Memoranda editorial table):

BROMLEY On the 29th inst., of consumption, Philip Bromley, in the 50th year of his age.

Affliction sore long time he bore,
  Physicians were in vain –
Till God at last did hear him mourn,
  And eased him of his pain.

The friend whom death from us has torn,
  We did not think so soon to part;
An anxious care now sinks the thorn
  Still deeper in our bleeding heart.

This beautiful creation loses nothing by repetition. On the contrary, the oftener one sees it in the *Ledger*, the more grand and awe-inspiring it seems.

With one more extract I will close:

DOBLE On the 4th inst., Samuel Peveril Worthington Doble, aged 4 days.

Our little Sammy's gone,
  His tiny spirit's fled;
Our little boy we loved so dear
  Lies sleeping with the dead.

> A tear within a father's eye,
> A mother's aching heart,
> Can only tell the agony
> How hard it is to part.

Could anything be more plaintive than that, without requiring further concessions of grammar? Could anything be likely to
do more toward reconciling the deceased to circumstances, and
making him willing to go? Perhaps not. The power of song can
hardly be estimated. There is an element about some poetry
which is able to make even physical suffering and death cheerful
things to contemplate and consummations to be desired. This
element is present in the mortuary poetry of Philadelphia degree
of development.

The custom I have been treating of is one that should be
adopted in all the cities of the land.

It is said that once a man of small consequence died, and the
Rev. T. K. Beecher was asked to preach the funeral sermon – a
man who abhors the lauding of people, either dead or alive,
except in dignified and simple language, and then only for
merits which they actually possessed or possess, not merits
which they merely ought to have possessed. The friends of the
deceased got up a stately funeral. They must have had misgiv-
ings that the corpse might not be praised strongly enough, for
they prepared some manuscript headings and notes in which
nothing was left unsaid on that subject that a fervid imagination
and an unabridged dictionary could compile, and these they
handed to the minister as he entered the pulpit. They were
merely intended as suggestions, and so the friends were filled
with consternation when the minister stood up in the pulpit
and proceeded to read off the curious odds and ends in ghastly
detail and in a loud voice! And their consternation solidified to
petrification when he paused at the end, contemplated the multitude reflectively, and then said, impressively:

'The man would be a fool who tried to add anything to that.
Let us pray!'

And with the same strict adhesion to truth it can be said that
the man would be a fool who tried to add anything to the
following transcendent obituary poem. There is something so

innocent, so guileless, so complacent, so unearthly serene and self-satisfied about this peerless 'hog-wash', that the man must be made of stone who can read it without a dulcet ecstasy creeping along his backbone and quivering in his marrow. There is no need to say that this poem is genuine and in earnest, for its proofs are written all over its face. An ingenious scribbler might imitate it after a fashion, but Shakespeare himself could not counterfeit it. It is noticeable that the country editor who published it did not know that it was a treasure and the most perfect thing of its kind that the storehouses and museums of literature could show. He did not dare to say no to the dread poet – for such a poet must have been something of an apparition – but he just shoveled it into his paper anywhere that came handy, and felt ashamed, and put that disgusted 'Published by Request' over it, and hoped that his subscribers would overlook it or not feel an impulse to read it:

Published by Request

LINES

*Composed on the death of Samuel and
Catharine Belkman's children.*

BY M. A. GLAZE

Friends and neighbors all draw near,
  And listen to what I have to say;
And never leave your children dear
  When they are small, and go away.

But always think of that sad fate,
  That happened in year of '63;
Four children with a house did burn,
  Think of their awful agony.

Their mother she had gone away,
  And left them there alone to stay;
The house took fire and down did burn,
  Before their mother did return.

227

Their piteous cry the neighbors heard,
　And then the cry of fire was given;
But, ah! before they could them reach,
　Their little spirits had flown to heaven.

Their father he to war had gone,
　And on the battlefield was slain;
But little did he think when he went away,
　But what on earth they would meet again.

The neighbors often told his wife
　Not to leave his children there,
Unless she got someone to stay,
　And of the little ones take care.

The oldest he was years not six,
　And the youngest only eleven months old,
But often she had left them there alone,
　As, by the neighbors, I have been told.

How can she bear to see the place,
　Where she so oft has left them there,
Without a single one to look to them,
　Or of the little ones to take good care.

Oh, can she look upon the spot,
　Whereunder their little burnt bones lay,
But what she thinks she hears them say,
　' 'Twas God had pity, and took us on high.'

And there may she kneel down and pray,
　And ask God her to forgive;
And she may lead a different life
　While she on earth remains to live.

Her husband and her children too,
　God has took from pain and woe.
May she reform and mend her ways,
　That she may also to them go.

And when it is God's holy will,
   O, may she be prepared
To meet her God and friends in peace,
   And leave this world of care.

What Hank Said to Horace Greeley

On the western verge of the desert we halted a moment at Rag-town. It consisted of one log house and is not set down on the map.

This reminds me of a circumstance. Just after we left Jules-burg, on the Platte, I was sitting with the driver, and he said:

'I can tell you a most laughable thing indeed, if you would like to listen to it. Horace Greeley went over this road once. When he was leaving Carson City he told the driver, Hank Monk, that he had an engagement to lecture at Placerville and was very anxious to go through quick. Hank Monk cracked his whip and started off at an awful pace. The coach bounced up and down in such a terrific way that it jolted the buttons all off of Horace's coat, and finally shot his head clean through the roof of the stage, and then he yelled at Hank Monk and begged him to go easier – said he warn't in as much of a hurry as he was awhile ago. But Hank Monk said, "Keep your seat, Horace, and I'll get you there on time" – and you bet you he did, too, what was left of him!'

A day or two after that we picked up a Denver man at the crossroads, and he told us a good deal about the country and the Gregory Diggings. He seemed a very entertaining person and a man well posted in the affairs of Colorado. By and by he remarked:

'I can tell you a most laughable thing indeed, if you would like to listen to it. Horace Greeley went over this road once. When he was leaving Carson City he told the driver, Hank Monk, that he had an engagement to lecture at Placerville and was very anxious to go through quick. Hank Monk cracked his whip and started off at an awful pace. The coach bounced up and down in such a terrific way that it jolted the buttons all off of Horace's coat, and finally shot his head clean through the roof of the stage, and then he yelled at Hank Monk and begged him to go easier – said he warn't in as much of a hurry as he was awhile ago. But Hank Monk said, "Keep your seat, Horace, and I'll get you there on time" – and you bet you he did, too, what was left of him!'

At Fort Bridger, some days after this, we took on board a cavalry sergeant, a very proper and soldierly person indeed. From no other man during the whole journey did we gather such a store of concise and well-arranged military information. It was surprising to find in the desolate wilds of our country a man so thoroughly acquainted with everything useful to know in his line of life, and yet of such inferior rank and unpretentious bearing. For as much as three hours we listened to him with unabated interest. Finally he got upon the subject of transcontinental travel, and presently said:

'I can tell you a very laughable thing indeed, if you would like to listen to it. Horace Greeley went over this road once. When he was leaving Carson City he told the driver, Hank Monk, that he had an engagement to lecture at Placerville and was very anxious to go through quick. Hank Monk cracked his whip and started off at an awful pace. The coach bounced up and down in such a terrific way that it jolted the buttons all off of Horace's coat, and finally shot his head clean through the roof of the stage, and then he yelled at Hank Monk and begged him to go easier – said he warn't in as much of a hurry as he was awhile ago. But Hank Monk said, "Keep your seat, Horace, and I'll get you there on time" – and you bet you he did, too, what was left of him!'

When we were eight hours out from Salt Lake City a Mormon preacher got in with us at a way-station – a gentle, soft-spoken, kindly man, and one whom any stranger would warm to at first sight. I can never forget the pathos that was in his voice as he told, in simple language, the story of his people's wanderings and unpitied sufferings. No pulpit eloquence was ever so moving and so beautiful as this outcast's picture of the first Mormon pilgrimage across the plains, struggling sorrowfully onward to the land of its banishment and marking its desolate way with graves and watering it with tears. His words so wrought upon us that it was a relief to us all when the conversation drifted into a more cheerful channel and the natural features of the curious country we were in came under treatment. One matter after another was pleasantly discussed, and at length the stranger said:

'I can tell you a most laughable thing indeed, if you would like to listen to it. Horace Greeley went over this road once. When he was leaving Carson City he told the driver, Hank Monk, that he had an engagement to lecture in Placerville, and was very anxious to go through quick. Hank Monk cracked his whip and started off at an awful pace. The coach bounced up and down in such a terrific way that it jolted the buttons all off of Horace's coat, and finally shot his head clean through the roof of the stage, and then he yelled at Hank Monk and begged him to go easier – said he warn't in as much of a hurry as he was awhile ago. But Hank Monk said, "Keep your seat, Horace, and I'll get you there on time" – and you bet you he did, too, what was left of him!'

Ten miles out of Ragtown we found a poor wanderer who had lain down to die. He had walked as long as he could, but his limbs had failed him at last. Hunger and fatigue had conquered him. It would have been inhuman to leave him there. We paid his fare to Carson and lifted him into the coach. It was some little time before he showed any very decided signs of life; but by dint of chafing him and pouring brandy between his lips we finally brought him to a languid consciousness. Then we fed him a little, and by and by he seemed to comprehend the situation and a grateful light softened his eye. We made his mail-sack bed as comfortable as possible, and constructed a pillow for him with our coats. He seemed very thankful. Then he looked up in our faces, and said in a feeble voice that had a tremble of honest emotion in it:

'Gentlemen, I know not who you are, but you have saved my life; and although I can never be able to repay you for it, I feel that I can at least make one hour of your long journey lighter. I take it you are strangers to this great thoroughfare, but I am entirely familiar with it. In this connection I can tell you a most laughable thing indeed, if you would like to listen to it. Horace Greeley—'

I said, impressively:

'Suffering stranger, proceed at your peril. You see in me the melancholy wreck of a once stalwart and magnificent manhood.

What has brought me to this? That thing which you are about to tell. Gradually, but surely, that tiresome old anecdote has sapped my strength, undermined my constitution, withered my life. Pity my helplessness. Spare me only just this once, and tell me about young George Washington and his little hatchet for a change.'

We were saved. But not so the invalid. In trying to retain the anecdote in his system he strained himself and died in our arms.

I am aware, now, that I ought not to have asked of the sturdiest citizen of all that region, what I asked of that mere shadow of a man; for, after seven years' residence on the Pacific coast, I know that no passenger or driver on the Overland ever corked that anecdote in, when a stranger was by, and survived. Within a period of six years I crossed and recrossed the Sierras between Nevada and California thirteen times by stage and listened to that deathless incident four hundred and eighty-one or eighty-two times. I have the list somewhere. Drivers always told it, conductors told it, landlords told it, chance passengers told it, the very Chinamen and vagrant Indians recounted it. I have had the same driver tell it to me two or three times in the same afternoon. It has come to me in all the multitude of tongues that Babel bequeathed to earth, and flavored with whiskey, brandy, beer, cologne, sozodont, tobacco, garlic, onions, grasshoppers – everything that has a fragrance to it through all the long list of things that are gorged or guzzled by the sons of men. I never have smelt any anecdote as often as I have smelt that one; never have smelt any anecdote that smelt so variegated as that one. And you never could learn to know it by its smell, because every time you thought you had learned the smell of it, it would turn up with a different smell. Bayard Taylor has written about this hoary anecdote, Richardson has published it; so have Jones, Smith, Johnson, Ross Browne, and every other correspondence-inditing being that ever set his foot upon the great overland road anywhere between Julesburg and San Francisco; and I have heard that it is in the Talmud. I have seen it in print in nine different foreign languages; I have been told that it is employed in the inquisition in Rome; and I now learn with regret that it is going to be set to music. I do not think that such things are right.

233

Stage-coaching on the Overland is no more, and stage-drivers are a race defunct. I wonder if they bequeathed that bald-headed anecdote to their successors, the railroad brakemen and conductors, and if these latter still persecute the helpless passenger with it until he concludes, as did many a tourist of other days, that the real grandeurs of the Pacific coast are not Yo Semite and the Big Trees, but Hank Monk and his adventure with Horace Greeley.*

Roughing It

* And what makes that worn anecdote the more aggravating is, that the adventure it celebrates *never occurred*. If it were a good anecdote, that seeming demerit would be its chiefest virtue, for creative power belongs to greatness; but what ought to be done to a man who would wantonly contrive so flat a one as this? If *I* were to suggest what ought to be done to him, I should be called extravagant – but what does the sixteenth chapter of Daniel say? Aha!

About Magnanimous-Incident Literature

All my life, from boyhood up, I have had the habit of reading a certain set of anecdotes, written in the quaint vein of The World's ingenious Fabulist, for the lesson they taught me and the pleasure they gave me. They lay always convenient to my hand, and whenever I thought meanly of my kind I turned to them, and they banished that sentiment; whenever I felt myself to be selfish, sordid, and ignoble I turned to them, and they told me what to do to win back my self-respect. Many times I wished that the charming anecdotes had not stopped with their happy climaxes, but had continued the pleasing history of the several benefactors and beneficiaries. This wish rose in my breast so persistently that at last I determined to satisfy it by seeking out the sequels of those anecdotes myself. So I set about it, and after great labor and tedious research accomplished my task. I will lay the result before you, giving you each anecdote in its turn, and following it with its sequel as I gathered it through my investigations.

THE GRATEFUL POODLE

One day a benevolent physician (who had read the books) having found a stray poodle suffering from a broken leg, conveyed the poor creature to his home, and after setting and bandaging the injured limb gave the little outcast its liberty again, and thought no more about the matter. But how great was his surprise, upon opening his door one morning, some days later, to find the grateful poodle patiently waiting there, and in its company another stray dog, one of whose legs, by some accident, had been broken. The kind physician at once relieved the distressed animal, nor did he forget to admire the inscrutable goodness and mercy of God, who had been willing to use so humble an instrument as the poor outcast poodle for the inculcating of, etc., etc., etc.

The next morning the benevolent physician found the two dogs, beaming with gratitude, waiting at his door, and with them two other dogs – cripples. The cripples were speedily healed, and the four went their way, leaving the benevolent physician more overcome by pious wonder than ever. The day passed, the morning came. There at the door sat now the four reconstructed dogs, and with them four others requiring reconstruction. This day also passed, and another morning came; and now sixteen dogs, eight of them newly crippled, occupied the sidewalk, and the people were going around. By noon the broken legs were all set, but the pious wonder in the good physician's breast was beginning to get mixed with involuntary profanity. The sun rose once more, and exhibited thirty-two dogs, sixteen of them with broken legs, occupying the sidewalk and half of the street; the human spectators took up the rest of the room. The cries of the wounded, the songs of the healed brutes, and the comments of the onlooking citizens made great and inspiring cheer, but traffic was interrupted in that street. The good physician hired a couple of assistant surgeons and got through his benevolent work before dark, first taking the precaution to cancel his church-membership, so that he might express himself with the latitude which the case required.

But some things have their limits. When once more the morning dawned, and the good physician looked out upon a massed and far-reaching multitude of clamorous and beseeching dogs, he said, 'I might as well acknowledge it, I have been fooled by the books; they only tell the pretty part of the story, and then stop. Fetch me the shotgun; this thing has gone along far enough.'

He issued forth with his weapon, and chanced to step upon the tail of the original poodle, who promptly bit him in the leg. Now the great and good work which this poodle had been engaged in had engendered in him such a mighty and augmenting enthusiasm as to turn his weak head at last and drive him mad. A month later, when the benevolent physician lay in the death-throes of hydrophobia, he called his weeping friends about him, and said:

'Beware of the books. They tell but half of the story. Whenever a poor wretch asks you for help, and you feel a doubt as to what result may flow from your benevolence, give yourself the benefit of the doubt and kill the applicant.'

And so saying he turned his face to the wall and gave up the ghost.

THE BENEVOLENT AUTHOR

A poor and young literary beginner had tried in vain to get his manuscripts accepted. At last, when the horrors of starvation were staring him in the face, he laid his sad case before a celebrated author, beseeching his counsel and assistance. This generous man immediately put aside his own matters and proceeded to peruse one of the despised manuscripts. Having completed his kindly task, he shook the poor young man cordially by the hand, saying, 'I perceive merit in this; come again to me on Monday.' At the time specified, the celebrated author, with a sweet smile, but saying nothing, spread open a magazine which was damp from the press. What was the poor young man's astonishment to discover upon the printed page his own article. 'How can I ever', said he, falling upon his knees and bursting into tears, 'testify my gratitude for this noble conduct!'

The celebrated author was the renowned Snodgrass; the poor young beginner thus rescued from obscurity and starvation was the afterward equally renowned Snagsby. Let this pleasing incident admonish us to turn a charitable ear to all beginners that need help.

SEQUEL

The next week Snagsby was back with five rejected manuscripts. The celebrated author was a little surprised, because in the books the young struggler had needed but one lift, apparently. However, he plowed through these papers, removing unnecessary flowers and digging up some acres of adjective stumps, and then succeeded in getting two of the articles accepted.

A week or so drifted by, and the grateful Snagsby arrived with another cargo. The celebrated author had felt a mighty glow of satisfaction within himself the first time he had successfully befriended the poor young struggler, and had compared himself with the generous people in the books with high gratification; but he was beginning to suspect now that he had struck upon something fresh in the noble-episode line. His enthusiasm took a chill. Still, he could not bear to repulse this struggling young author, who clung to him with such pretty simplicity and trustfulness.

Well, the upshot of it all was that the celebrated author presently found himself permanently freighted with the poor young beginner. All his mild efforts to unload this cargo went for nothing. He had to give daily counsel, daily encouragement; he had to keep on procuring magazine acceptances, and then revamping the manuscripts to make them presentable. When the young aspirant got a start at last, he rode into sudden fame by describing the celebrated author's private life with such a caustic humor and such minuteness of blistering detail that the book sold a prodigious edition, and broke the celebrated author's heart with mortification. With his latest gasp he said, 'Alas, the books deceived me; they do not tell the whole story. Beware of the struggling young author, my friends. Whom God sees fit to starve, let not man presumptuously rescue to his own undoing.'

THE GRATEFUL HUSBAND

One day a lady was driving through the principal street of a great city with her little boy, when the horses took fright and dashed madly away, hurling the coachman from his box and leaving the occupants of the carriage paralyzed with terror. But a brave youth who was driving a grocery-wagon threw himself before the plunging animals, and succeeded in arresting their flight at the peril of his own.* The grateful lady took his number, and upon arriving at her home she related the heroic act to her husband (who had read the books), who listened with streaming eyes to the moving recital, and who, after returning thanks, in conjunction with his restored loved ones, to Him who suffereth not even a sparrow to fall to the ground unnoticed, sent for the brave young person, and, placing a check for five hundred dollars in his hand, said, 'Take this as a reward for your noble act, William Ferguson, and if ever you shall need

* This is probably a misprint. M. T.

238

a friend, remember that Thompson McSpadden has a grateful heart.' Let us learn from this that a good deed cannot fail to benefit the doer, however humble he may be.

William Ferguson called the next week and asked Mr McSpadden to use his influence to get him a higher employment, he feeling capable of better things than driving a grocer's wagon. Mr McSpadden got him an underclerkship at a good salary.

Presently William Ferguson's mother fell sick, and William— Well, to cut the story short, Mr McSpadden consented to take her into his house. Before long she yearned for the society of her younger children; so Mary and Julia were admitted also, and little Jimmy, their brother. Jimmy had a pocketknife, and he wandered into the drawing-room with it one day, alone, and reduced ten thousand dollars' worth of furniture to an indeterminable value in rather less than three-quarters of an hour. A day or two later he fell downstairs and broke his neck, and seventeen of his family's relatives came to the house to attend the funeral. This made them acquainted, and they kept the kitchen occupied after that, and likewise kept the McSpaddens busy hunting up situations of various sorts for them, and hunting up more when they wore these out. The old woman drank a good deal and swore a good deal; but the grateful McSpaddens knew it was their duty to reform her, considering what her son had done for them, so they clave nobly to their generous task. William came often and got decreasing sums of money, and asked for higher and more lucrative employments – which the grateful McSpadden more or less promptly procured for him. McSpadden consented also, after some demur, to fit William for college; but when the first vacation came and the hero requested to be sent to Europe for his health, the persecuted McSpadden rose against the tyrant and revolted. He plainly and squarely refused. William Ferguson's mother was so astounded that she let her gin-bottle drop, and her profane lips refused to do their office. When she recovered she said in a half-gasp, 'Is this your gratitude? Where would your wife and boy be now, but for my son?'

William said, 'Is this your gratitude? Did I save your wife's life or not? Tell me that!'

Seven relations swarmed in from the kitchen and each said, 'And this is his gratitude!'

William's sisters stared, bewildered, and said, 'And this is his grat—' but were interrupted by their mother, who burst into tears and exclaimed, 'To think that my sainted little Jimmy threw away his life in the service of such a reptile!'

Then the pluck of the revolutionary McSpadden rose to the occasion, and he replied with fervor, 'Out of my house, the whole beggarly tribe of you! I was beguiled by the books, but shall never be beguiled again – once is sufficient for me.' And turning to William he shouted, 'Yes, you did save my wife's life, and the next man that does it shall die in his tracks!'

Not being a clergyman, I place my text at the end of my sermon instead of at the beginning. Here it is, from Mr Noah Brooks's 'Recollections of President Lincoln' in *Scribner's Monthly*:

J. H. Hackett, in his part of Falstaff, was an actor who gave Mr Lincoln great delight. With his usual desire to signify to others his sense of obligation, Mr Lincoln wrote a genial little note to the actor expressing his pleasure at witnessing his performance. Mr Hackett, in reply, sent a book of some sort; perhaps it was one of his own authorship. He also wrote several notes to the President. One night, quite late, when the episode had passed out of my mind, I went to the White House in answer to a message. Passing into the President's office, I noticed, to my surprise, Hackett sitting in the anteroom as if waiting for an audience. The President asked me if anyone was outside. On being told, he said, half sadly, 'Oh, I can't see him, I can't see him; I was in hopes he had gone away.' Then he added, 'Now this just illustrates the difficulty of having pleasant friends and acquaintances in this place. You know how I liked Hackett as an actor, and how I wrote to tell him so. He sent me that book, and there I thought the matter would end. He is a master of his place in the profession, I suppose, and well fixed in it; but just because we had a little friendly correspondence, such as any two men might have, he wants something. What do you suppose he wants?' I could not guess, and Mr Lincoln added, 'Well, he wants to be consul to London. Oh, dear!'

I will observe, in conclusion, that the William Ferguson incident occurred, and within my personal knowledge – though I have changed the nature of the details, to keep William from recognizing himself in it.

All the readers of this article have in some sweet and gushing hour of their lives played the role of Magnanimous-Incident hero. I wish I knew how many there are among them who are willing to talk about that episode and like to be reminded of the consequences that flowed from it.

On the Decay
of the Art of Lying

*Essay, for Discussion, Read at a Meeting of the Historical and
Antiquarian Club of Hartford, and Offered for the
Thirty-Dollar Prize. Now First Published**

Observe, I do not mean to suggest that the *custom* of lying has
suffered any decay or interruption – no, for the Lie, as a Virtue, a
Principle, is eternal; the Lie, as a recreation, a solace, a refuge in
time of need, the fourth Grace, the tenth Muse, man's best and
surest friend, is immortal, and cannot perish from the earth
while this Club remains. My complaint simply concerns the
decay of the *art* of lying. No high-minded man, no man of right
feeling, can contemplate the lumbering and slovenly lying of
the present day without grieving to see a noble art so prosti-
tuted. In this veteran presence I naturally enter upon this
scheme with diffidence; it is like an old maid trying to teach
nursery matters to the mothers in Israel. It would not become
me to criticize you, gentlemen, who are nearly all my elders –
and my superiors, in this thing – and so, if I should here and
there *seem* to do it, I trust it will in most cases be more in a spirit
of admiration than of fault-finding; indeed, if this finest of the
fine arts had everywhere received the attention, encouragement, and conscientious practice and development which this
Club has devoted to it, I should not need to utter this lament or
shed a single tear. I do not say this to flatter: I say it in a spirit of
just and appreciative recognition.

[It had been my intention, at this point, to mention names
and give illustrative specimens, but indications observable
about me admonished me to beware of particulars and confine
myself to generalities.]

No fact is more firmly established than that lying is a necessity of our circumstances – the deduction that it is then a Virtue
goes without saying. No virtue can reach its highest usefulness

* Did not take the prize.

without careful and diligent cultivation – therefore, it goes without saying that this one ought to be taught in the public schools – at the fireside – even in the newspapers. What chance has the ignorant, uncultivated liar against the educated expert? What chance have I against Mr Per— against a lawyer? *Judicious* lying is what the world needs. I sometimes think it were even better and safer not to lie at all than to lie injudiciously. An awkward, unscientific lie is often as ineffectual as the truth.

Now let us see what the philosophers say. Note that venerable proverb: Children and fools *always* speak the truth. The deduction is plain – adults and wise persons never speak it. Parkman, the historian, says, 'The principle of truth may itself be carried into an absurdity.' In another place in the same chapter he says, 'The saying is old that truth should not be spoken at all times; and those whom a sick conscience worries into habitual violation of the maxim are imbeciles and nuisances.' It is strong language, but true. None of us could *live* with an habitual truth-teller; but, thank goodness, none of us has to. An habitual truth-teller is simply an impossible creature; he does not exist; he never has existed. Of course there are people who *think* they never lie, but it is not so – and this ignorance is one of the very things that shame our so-called civilization. Everybody lies – every day; every hour; awake; asleep; in his dreams; in his joy; in his mourning; if he keeps his tongue still, his hands, his feet, his eyes, his attitude, will convey deception – and purposely. Even in sermons – but that is a platitude.

In a far country where I once lived the ladies used to go around paying calls, under the humane and kindly pretense of wanting to see each other; and when they returned home, they would cry out with a glad voice, saying, 'We made sixteen calls and found fourteen of them out' – not meaning that they found out anything against the fourteen – no, that was only a colloquial phrase to signify that they were not at home – and their manner of saying it expressed their lively satisfaction in that fact. Now their pretense of wanting to see the fourteen – and the other two whom they had been less lucky with – was that commonest and mildest form of lying which is sufficiently described as a deflection from the truth. Is it justifiable? Most certainly. It is beautiful, it is noble; for its object is, *not* to reap profit, but to convey a pleasure to the sixteen. The iron-souled truth-monger would plainly manifest, or even utter the fact, that he didn't want to see those people – and he would be an ass, and inflict a totally unnecessary pain. And next, those ladies in that far country – but never mind, they had a thousand pleasant ways of lying, that grew out of gentle impulses, and were a credit to their intelligence and an honor to their hearts. Let the particulars go.

The men in that far country were liars, every one. Their mere howdy-do was a lie, because *they* didn't care how you did, except they were undertakers. To the ordinary inquirer you lied in return; for you made no conscientious diagnosis of your case, but answered at random, and usually missed it considerably. You lied to the undertaker, and said your health was failing – a wholly commendable lie, since it cost you nothing and pleased the other man. If a stranger called and interrupted you, you said with your hearty tongue, 'I'm glad to see you,' and said with your heartier soul, 'I wish you were with the cannibals and it was dinner-time.' When he went, you said regretfully, '*Must* you go?' and followed it with a 'Call again'; but you did no harm, for you did not deceive anybody nor inflict any hurt, whereas the truth would have made you both unhappy.

I think that all this courteous lying is a sweet and loving art, and should be cultivated. The highest perfection of politeness is only a beautiful edifice, built, from the base to the dome, of graceful and gilded forms of charitable and unselfish lying.

What I bemoan is the growing prevalence of the brutal truth. Let us do what we can to eradicate it. An injurious truth has no merit over an injurious lie. Neither should ever be uttered. The man who speaks an injurious truth, lest his soul be not saved if he do otherwise, should reflect that that sort of a soul is not strictly worth saving. The man who tells a lie to help a poor devil out of trouble is one of whom the angels doubtless say, 'Lo, here is an heroic soul who casts his own welfare into jeopardy to succor his neighbor's; let us exalt this magnanimous liar.'

An injurious lie is an uncommendable thing; and so, also, and in the same degree, is an injurious truth – a fact which is recognized by the law of libel.

Among other common lies, we have the *silent* lie – the deception which one conveys by simply keeping still and concealing the truth. Many obstinate truth-mongers indulge in this dissipation, imagining that if they *speak* no lie, they lie not at all. In that far country where I once lived, there was a lovely spirit, a lady whose impulses were always high and pure, and whose character answered to them. One day I was there at dinner, and remarked, in a general way, that we are all liars. She was amazed, and said, 'Not *all!*' It was before *Pinafore's* time, so I did not make the response which would naturally follow in our day, but frankly said, 'Yes, *all* – we are all liars; there are no exceptions.' She looked almost offended, and said, 'Why, do you include *me?*' 'Certainly,' I said, 'I think you even rank as an expert.' She said, ' 'Sh! – 'sh! the children!' So the subject was changed in deference to the children's presence, and we went on talking about other things. But as soon as the young people were out of the way, the lady came warmly back to the matter and said, 'I have made it the rule of my life to never tell a lie; and I have never departed from it in a single instance.' I said, 'I don't mean the least harm or disrespect, but really you have been lying like smoke ever since I've been sitting here. It has caused me a good deal of pain, because I am not used to it.' She required of me an instance – just a single instance. So I said:

'Well, here is the unfilled duplicate of the blank which the Oakland hospital people sent to you by the hand of the sick-nurse when she came here to nurse your little nephew through his dangerous illness. This blank asks all manner of questions as to the conduct of that sick-nurse: "Did she ever sleep on her watch? Did she ever forget to give the medicine?" and so forth and so on. You are warned to be very careful and explicit in your answers, for the welfare of the service requires that the nurses be promptly fined or otherwise punished for derelictions. You told me you were perfectly delighted with that nurse – that she had a thousand perfections and only one fault: you found you never could depend on her wrapping Johnny up half sufficiently while he waited in a chilly chair for her to rearrange the warm bed. You filled up the duplicate of this paper, and sent it back to the hospital by the hand of the nurse. How did you answer this question – "Was the nurse at any time guilty of a negligence which was likely to result in the patient's taking cold?" Come – everything is decided by a bet here in California: ten dollars to ten cents you lied when you answered that question.' She said, 'I didn't; *I left it blank!*' 'Just so – you have told a *silent* lie; you have left it to be inferred that you had no fault to find in that matter.' She said, 'Oh, was that a lie? And how *could* I mention her one single fault, and she so good? – it would have been cruel.' I said, 'One ought always to lie when one can do good by it; your impulse was right, but your judgment was crude; this comes of unintelligent practice. Now observe the result of this inexpert deflection of yours. You know Mr Jones's Willie is lying very low with scarlet fever; well, your recommendation was so enthusiastic that that girl is there nursing him, and the worn-out family have all been trustingly sound asleep for the last fourteen hours, leaving their darling with full confidence in those fatal hands, because you, like young George Washington, have a reputa— However, if you are not going to have anything to do, I will come around tomorrow and we'll attend the funeral together, for, of course, you'll naturally feel a peculiar interest in Willie's case – as personal a one, in fact, as the undertaker.'

But that was all lost. Before I was halfway through she was in a carriage and making thirty miles an hour toward the Jones mansion to save what was left of Willie and tell all she knew about the deadly nurse. All of which was unnecessary, as Willie wasn't sick; I had been lying myself. But that same day, all the same, she sent a line to the hospital which filled up the neglected blank, and stated the *facts*, too, in the squarest possible manner.

Now, you see, this lady's fault was *not* in lying, but only in lying injudiciously. She should have told the truth, *there*, and made it up to the nurse with a fraudulent compliment further along in the paper. She could have said, 'In one respect the sick-nurse is perfection – when she is on watch, she never snores.' Almost any little pleasant lie would have taken the sting out of that troublesome but necessary expression of the truth.

Lying is universal – we *all* do it; we all *must* do it. Therefore, the wise thing is for us diligently to train ourselves to lie thoughtfully, judiciously; to lie with a good object, and not an evil one; to lie for others' advantage, and not our own; to lie healingly, charitably, humanely, not cruelly, hurtfully, maliciously; to lie gracefully and graciously, not awkwardly and

246

clumsily; to lie firmly, frankly, squarely, with head erect, not haltingly, tortuously, with pusillanimous mien, as being ashamed of our high calling. Then shall we be rid of the rank and pestilent truth that is rotting the land; then shall we be great and good and beautiful, and worthy dwellers in a world where even benign Nature habitually lies, except when she promises execrable weather. Then— But I am but a new and feeble student in this gracious art; I cannot instruct *this* Club.

Joking aside, I think there is much need of wise examination into what sorts of lies are best and wholesomest to be indulged, seeing we *must* all lie and *do* all lie, and what sorts it may be best to avoid – and this is a thing which I feel I can confidently put into the hands of this experienced Club – a ripe body, who may be termed, in this regard, and without undue flattery, Old Masters.

The Private History
of a Campaign That Failed

You have heard from a great many people who did something in the war; is it not fair and right that you listen a little moment to one who started out to do something in it, but didn't? Thousands entered the war, got just a taste of it, and then stepped out again, permanently. These, by their very numbers, are respectable, and are therefore entitled to a sort of voice, not a loud one, but a modest one; not a boastful one, but an apologetic one. They ought not to be allowed much space among better people – people who did something – I grant that; but they ought at least to be allowed to state why they didn't do anything, and also to explain the process by which they didn't do anything. Surely this kind of light must have a sort of value.

Out West there was a good deal of confusion in men's minds during the first months of the great trouble, a good deal of unsettledness, of leaning first this way, then that, then the other way. It was hard for us to get our bearings. I call to mind an instance of this. I was piloting on the Mississippi when the news came that South Carolina had gone out of the Union on the 20th of December, 1860. My pilot-mate was a New Yorker. He was strong for the Union; so was I. But he would not listen to me with any patience; my loyalty was smirched, to his eye, because my father had owned slaves. I said, in palliation of this dark fact, that I had heard my father say, some years before he died, that slavery was a great wrong, and that he would free the solitary negro he then owned if he could think it right to give away the property of the family when he was so straitened in means. My mate retorted that a mere impulse was nothing – anybody could pretend to a good impulse; and went on decrying my Unionism and libeling my ancestry. A month later the secession atmosphere had considerably thickened on the Lower Mississippi, and I became a rebel; so did he. We were together in New Orleans, the 26th of January, when Louisiana went out of the Union. He did his full share of the rebel shouting, but was bitterly opposed to letting me do mine. He said that I came of bad stock – of a father who had been willing to set slaves free. In the following summer he was piloting a Federal gun-boat and shouting for the Union again, and I was in the Confederate army. I held his note for some borrowed money. He was one of the most upright men I ever knew; but he repudiated that note without hesitation, because I was a rebel, and the son of a man who owned slaves.

In that summer – of 1861 – the first wash of the wave of war broke upon the shores of Missouri. Our State was invaded by the Union forces. They took possession of St Louis, Jefferson Barracks, and some other points. The Governor, Claib Jackson, issued his proclamation calling out fifty thousand militia to repel the invader.

I was visiting in the small town where my boyhood had been spent – Hannibal, Marion County. Several of us got together in a secret place by night and formed ourselves into a military company. One Tom Lyman, a young fellow of a good deal of spirit but of no military experience, was made captain; I was made second lieutenant. We had no first lieutenant; I do not know why; it was long ago. There were fifteen of us. By the advice of an innocent connected with the organization, we called ourselves the Marion Rangers. I do not remember that anyone found fault with the name. I did not; I thought it sounded quite well. The young fellow who proposed this title was perhaps a fair sample of the kind of stuff we were made of. He was young, ignorant, good-natured, well-meaning, trivial, full of romance, and given to reading chivalric novels and singing forlorn love-ditties. He had some pathetic little nickel-plated aristocratic instincts, and detested his name, which was Dunlap; detested it, partly because it was nearly as common in that region as Smith, but mainly because it had a plebeian sound to his ear. So he tried to ennoble it by writing it in this way: *d'Unlap*. That contented his eye, but left his ear unsatisfied, for people gave the new name the same old pronunciation – emphasis on the front end of it. He then did the bravest thing that can be imagined, a thing to make one shiver when one remembers how the world is given to resenting shams and affectations; he began to write his name so: *d'Un Lap*. And he waited patiently through the long storm of mud that was flung at this work of art, and he had his reward at last; for he lived to see that name accepted, and the emphasis put where he wanted it, by people who had known him all his life, and to whom the tribe of Dunlaps had been as familiar as the rain and the sunshine for forty years. So sure of victory at last is the courage that can wait. He said he had found, by consulting some ancient French chronicles, that the name was rightly and originally written d'Un Lap; and said that if it were translated into English it would mean Peterson: *Lap*, Latin or Greek, he said, for stone or rock, same as the French *pierre*, that is to say, Peter; *d'*, of or from; *un*, a or one; hence, d'Un Lap, of or from a stone or a Peter; that is to say, one who is the son of a stone, the son of a Peter – Peterson. Our militia company were not learned, and the explanation confused them; so they called him Peterson Dunlap. He proved useful to us in his way; he named our camps for us, and he generally struck a name that was 'no slouch', as the boys said.

That is one sample of us. Another was Ed Stevens, son of the town jeweler, trim-built, handsome, graceful, neat as a cat; bright, educated, but given over entirely to fun. There was nothing serious in life to him. As far as he was concerned, this military expedition of ours was simply a holiday. I should say that about half of us looked upon it in the same way; not consciously, perhaps, but unconsciously. We did not think; we were not capable of it. As for myself, I was full of unreasoning joy to be done with turning out of bed at midnight and four in the morning, for a while; grateful to have a change, new scenes, new occupations, a new interest. In my thoughts that was as far as I went; I did not go into the details; as a rule one doesn't at twenty-four.

Another sample was Smith, the blacksmith's apprentice. This vast donkey had some pluck, of a slow and sluggish nature, but a soft heart; at one time he would knock a horse down for some impropriety, and at another he would get homesick and cry. However, he had one ultimate credit to his account which some of us hadn't: he stuck to the war, and was killed in battle at last.

Jo Bowers, another sample, was a huge, good-natured, flax-headed lubber; lazy, sentimental, full of harmless brag, a grumbler by nature; an experienced, industrious, ambitious, and often quite picturesque liar, and yet not a successful one, for he had had no intelligent training, but was allowed to come up just any way. This life was serious enough to him, and seldom satisfactory. But he was a good fellow anyway, and the boys all liked him. He was made orderly sergeant; Stevens was made corporal.

These samples will answer – and they are quite fair ones. Well, this herd of cattle started for the war. What could you expect of them? They did as well as they knew how, but really what was justly to be expected of them? Nothing, I should say. That is what they did.

We waited for a dark night, for caution and secrecy were necessary; then, toward midnight, we stole in couples and from various directions to the Griffith place, beyond the town; from that point we set out together on foot. Hannibal lies at the extreme south-eastern corner of Marion County, on the Mississippi River; our objective point was the hamlet of New London, ten miles away, in Ralls County.

The first hour was all fun, all idle nonsense and laughter. But that could not be kept up. The steady trudging came to be like work; the play had somehow oozed out of it; the stillness of the woods and the somberness of the night began to throw a depressing influence over the spirits of the boys, and presently the talking died out and each person shut himself up in his own thoughts. During the last half of the second hour nobody said a word.

Now we approached a log farm-house where, according to report, there was a guard of five Union soldiers. Lyman called a halt; and there, in the deep gloom of the overhanging branches, he began to whisper a plan of assault upon that house, which made the gloom more depressing than it was before. It was a crucial moment; we realized, with a cold suddenness, that here was no jest – we were standing face to face with actual war. We were equal to the occasion. In our response there was no hesitation, no indecision: we said that if Lyman wanted to meddle with those soldiers, he could go ahead and do it; but if he waited for us to follow him, he would wait a long time.

Lyman urged, pleaded, tried to shame us, but it had no effect. Our course was plain, our minds were made up: we would flank the farm-house – go out around. And that is what we did.

We struck into the woods and entered upon a rough time, stumbling over roots, getting tangled in vines, and torn by briers. At last we reached an open place in a safe region, and sat down, blown and hot, to cool off and nurse our scratches and bruises. Lyman was annoyed, but the rest of us were cheerful; we had flanked the farm-house, we had made our first military movement, and it was a success; we had nothing to fret about, we were feeling just the other way. Horse-play and laughing began again; the expedition was become a holiday frolic once more.

Then we had two more hours of dull trudging and ultimate silence and depression; then, about dawn, we straggled into New London, soiled, heel-blistered, fagged with our little march, and all of us except Stevens in a sour and raspy humor and privately down on the war. We stacked our shabby old shotguns in Colonel Ralls's barn, and then went in a body and breakfasted with that veteran of the Mexican War. Afterwards he took us to a distant meadow, and there in the shade of a tree we listened to an old-fashioned speech from him, full of gunpowder and glory, full of that adjective-piling, mixed metaphor, and windy declamation which was regarded as eloquence in that ancient time and that remote region; and then he swore us on the Bible to be faithful to the State of Missouri and drive all invaders from her soil, no matter whence they might come or under what flag they might march. This mixed us considerably, and we could not make out just what service we were embarked in; but Colonel Ralls, the practiced politician and phrase-juggler, was not similarly in doubt; he knew quite clearly that he had invested us in the cause of the Southern Confederacy. He closed the solemnities by belting around me the sword which his neighbor, Colonel Brown, had worn at Buena Vista and Molino del Rey; and he accompanied this act with another impressive blast.

Then we formed in line of battle and marched four miles to a shady and pleasant piece of woods on the border of the far-reaching expanses of a flowery prairie. It was an enchanting region for war – our kind of war.

We pierced the forest about half a mile, and took up a strong position, with some low, rocky, and wooded hills behind us, and a purling, limpid creek in front. Straightway half the command were in swimming, and the other half fishing. The ass with the French name gave this position a romantic title, but it was too long, so the boys shortened and simplified it to Camp Ralls.

We occupied an old maple-sugar camp, whose half-rotted troughs were still propped against the trees. A long corn-crib served for sleeping quarters for the battalion. On our left, half a mile away, was Mason's farm and house; and he was a friend to the cause. Shortly after noon the farmers began to arrive from several directions, with mules and horses for our use, and these they lent us for as long as the war might last, which they judged would be about three months. The animals were of all sizes, all colors, and all breeds. They were mainly young and frisky, and nobody in the command could stay on them long at a time; for we were town boys, and ignorant of horsemanship. The creature that fell to my share was a very small mule, and yet so quick and active that it could throw me without difficulty; and it did this whenever I got on it. Then it would bray – stretching its neck out, laying its ears back, and spreading its jaws till you could see down to its works. It was a disagreeable animal, in every way. If I took it by the bridle and tried to lead it off the grounds, it would sit down and brace back, and no one could budge it. However, I was not entirely destitute of military resources, and I did presently manage to spoil this game; for I had seen many a steamboat aground in my time, and knew a trick or two which even a grounded mule would be obliged to respect. There was a well by the corn-crib; so I substituted thirty fathom of rope for the bridle, and fetched him home with the windlass.

I will anticipate here sufficiently to say that we did learn to ride, after some days' practice, but never well. We could not learn to like our animals; they were not choice ones, and most of them had annoying peculiarities of one kind or another. Stevens's horse would carry him, when he was not noticing, under the huge excrescences which form on the trunks of oak-trees, and wipe him out of the saddle; in this way Stevens got several bad hurts. Sergeant Bowers's horse was very large and tall, with slim, long legs, and looked like a railroad bridge. His size enabled him to reach all about, and as far as he wanted to, with his head; so he was always biting Bowers's legs. On the march, in the sun, Bowers slept a good deal; and as soon as the horse recognized that he was asleep he would reach around and bite him on the leg. His legs were black and blue with bites. This was the only thing that could ever make him swear, but this always did; whenever the horse bit him he always swore, and of course Stevens, who laughed at everything, laughed at this, and would even get into such convulsions over it as to lose his balance and fall off his horse; and then Bowers, already irritated by the pain of the horse-bite, would resent the laughter with hard language, and there would be a quarrel; so that horse made no end of trouble and bad blood in the command.

However, I will get back to where I was – our first afternoon in the sugar camp. The sugar-troughs came very handy as horse-troughs, and we had plenty of corn to fill them with. I ordered Sergeant Bowers to feed my mule; but he said that if I reckoned he went to war to be dry-nurse to a mule, it wouldn't take me very long to find out my mistake. I believed that this was insubordination, but I was full of uncertainties about everything military, and so I let the thing pass, and went and ordered Smith, the blacksmith's apprentice, to feed the mule; but he merely gave me a large, cold, sarcastic grin, such as an ostensibly seven-year-old horse gives you when you lift his lip and find he is fourteen, and turned his back on me. I then went to the captain, and asked if it was not right and proper and military for me to have an orderly. He said it was, but as there was only one orderly in the corps, it was but right that he himself should have Bowers on his staff. Bowers said he wouldn't serve on anybody's staff; and if anybody thought he could make him, let him try it. So, of course, the thing had to be dropped; there was no other way.

Next, nobody would cook; it was considered a degradation; so we had no dinner. We lazied the rest of the pleasant afternoon away, some dozing under the trees, some smoking cob-pipes and talking sweethearts and war, some playing games. By late supper-time all hands were famished; and to meet the difficulty all hands turned to, on an equal footing, and gathered wood, built fires, and cooked the meal. Afterward everything was smooth for a while; then trouble broke out between the corporal and the sergeant, each claiming to rank the other. Nobody knew which was the higher office; so Lyman had to settle the matter by making the rank of both officers equal. The commander of an ignorant crew like that has many troubles and vexations which probably do not occur in the regular army at all. However, with the song-singing and yarn-spinning around the camp-fire, everything presently became serene again; and by and by we raked the corn down level in one end of the crib, and all went to bed on it, tying a horse to the door, so that he would neigh if anyone tried to get in.*

We had some horsemanship drill every forenoon; then, afternoons, we rode off here and there in squads a few miles, and visited the farmers' girls, and had a youthful good time, and got an honest good dinner or supper, and then home again to camp, happy and content.

For a time, life was idly delicious, it was perfect; there was nothing to mar it. Then came some farmers with an alarm one day. They said it was rumored that the enemy were advancing in our direction, from over Hyde's prairie. The result was a sharp stir among us, and general consternation. It was a rude awakening from our pleasant trance. The rumor was but a rumor – nothing definite about it; so, in the confusion, we did not know which way to retreat. Lyman was for not retreating at all, in these uncertain circumstances; but he found that if he tried to maintain that attitude he would fare badly, for the command were in no humor to put up with insubordination. So he yielded the point and called a council of war – to consist of himself and the three other officers; but the privates made such a fuss about being left out, that we had to allow them to remain, for they were already present, and doing the most of the talking too. The

* It was always my impression that that was what the horse was there for, and I know that it was also the impression of at least one other of the command, for we talked about it at the time, and admired the military ingenuity of the device; but when I was out West three years ago I was told by Mr A. G. Fuqua, a member of our company, that the horse was his, that the leaving him tied at the door was a matter of mere forgetfulness, and that to attribute it to intelligent invention was to give him quite too much credit. In support of his position, he called my attention to the suggestive fact that the artifice was not employed again. I had not thought of that before.

question was, which way to retreat; but all were so flurried that nobody seemed to have even a guess to offer. Except Lyman. He explained in a few calm words, that inasmuch as the enemy were approaching from over Hyde's prairie, our course was simple: all we had to do was not to retreat *toward* him; any other direction would answer our needs perfectly. Everybody saw in a moment how true this was, and how wise; so Lyman got a great many compliments. It was now decided that we should fall back on Mason's farm.

It was after dark by this time, and as we could not know how soon the enemy might arrive, it did not seem best to try to take the horses and things with us; so we only took the guns and ammunition, and started at once. The route was very rough and hilly and rocky, and presently the night grew very black and rain began to fall; so we had a troublesome time of it, struggling and stumbling along in the dark; and soon some person slipped and fell, and then the next person behind stumbled over him and fell, and so did the rest, one after the other; and then Bowers came with the keg of powder in his arms, whilst the command were all mixed together, arms and legs, on the muddy slope; and so he fell, of course, with the keg, and this started the whole detachment down the hill in a body, and they landed in the brook at the bottom in a pile, and each that was undermost pulling the hair and scratching and biting those that were on top of him; and those that were being scratched and bitten, scratching and biting the rest in their turn, and all saying they would die before they would ever go to war again if they ever got out of this brook this time, and the invader might rot for all they cared, and the country along with him – and all such talk as that, which was dismal to hear and take part in, in such smothered, low voices, and such a grisly dark place and so wet, and the enemy may be coming any moment.

The keg of powder was lost, and the guns too; so the growling and complaining continued straight along whilst the brigade pawed around the pasty hillside and slopped around in the brook hunting for these things; consequently we lost considerable time at this; and then we heard a sound, and held our breath and listened, and it seemed to be the enemy coming, though it could have been a cow, for it had a cough like a cow;

but we did not wait, but left a couple of guns behind and struck out for Mason's again as briskly as we could scramble along in the dark. But we got lost presently among the rugged little ravines, and wasted a deal of time finding the way again, so it was after nine when we reached Mason's stile at last; and then, before we could open our mouths to give the countersign, several dogs came bounding over the fence, with great riot and noise, and each of them took a soldier by the slack of his trousers and began to back away with him. We could not shoot the dogs without endangering the persons they were attached to; so we had to look on, helpless, at what was perhaps the most mortifying spectacle of the civil war. There was light enough, and to spare, for the Masons had now run out on the porch with candles in their hands. The old man and his son came and undid the dogs without difficulty, all but Bowers's; but they couldn't undo his dog, they didn't know his combination; he was of the bull kind, and seemed to be set with a Yale time-lock; but they got him loose at last with some scalding water, of which Bowers got his share and returned thanks. Peterson Dunlap afterwards made up a fine name for this engagement, and also for the night march which preceded it, but both have long ago faded out of my memory.

We now went into the house, and they began to ask us a world of questions, whereby it presently came out that we did not know anything concerning who or what we were running from; so the old gentleman made himself very frank, and said we were a curious breed of soldiers, and guessed we could be depended on to end up the war in time, because no government could stand the expense of the shoe-leather we should cost it trying to follow us around. 'Marion *Rangers*! good name, b'gosh!' said he. And wanted to know why we hadn't had a picket-guard at the place where the road entered the prairie, and why we hadn't sent out a scouting party to spy out the enemy and bring us an account of his strength, and so on, before jumping up and stampeding out of a strong position upon a mere vague rumor – and so on, and so forth, till he made us all feel shabbier than the dogs had done, not half so enthusiastically welcome. So we went to bed shamed and low-spirited; except Stevens. Soon Stevens began to devise a garment for Bowers which could be made to automatically display his battle-scars to the grateful, or conceal them from the envious, according to his occasions; but Bowers was in no humor for this, so there was a fight, and when it was over Stevens had some battle-scars of his own to think about.

Then we got a little sleep. But after all we had gone through, our activities were not over for the night; for about two o'clock in the morning we heard a shout of warning from down the lane, accompanied by a chorus from all the dogs, and in a moment everybody was up and flying around to find out what the alarm was about. The alarmist was a horseman who gave notice that a detachment of Union soldiers was on its way from Hannibal with orders to capture and hang any bands like ours which it could find, and said we had no time to lose. Farmer Mason was in a flurry this time, himself. He hurried us out of the house with all haste, and sent one of his negroes with us to show us where to hide ourselves and our tell-tale guns among the ravines half a mile away. It was raining heavily.

We struck down the lane, then across some rocky pasture-land which offered good advantages for stumbling; consequently we were down in the mud most of the time, and every time a man went down he blackguarded the war, and the people that started it, and everybody connected with it, and gave himself the master dose of all for being so foolish as to go into it. At last we reached the wooded mouth of a ravine, and there we huddled ourselves under the streaming trees, and sent the negro back home. It was a dismal and heart-breaking time. We were like to be drowned with the rain, deafened with the howling wind and the booming thunder, and blinded by the lightning. It was indeed a wild night. The drenching we were getting was misery enough, but a deeper misery still was the reflection that the halter might end us before we were a day older. A death of this shameful sort had not occurred to us as being among the possibilities of war. It took the romance all out of the campaign, and turned our dreams of glory into a repulsive nightmare. As for doubting that so barbarous an order had been given, not one of us did that.

The long night wore itself out at last, and then the negro came to us with the news that the alarm had manifestly been a false one, and that breakfast would soon be ready. Straightway we were light-hearted again, and the world was bright, and life as full of hope and promise as ever – for we were young then. How long ago that was! Twenty-four years.

The mongrel child of philology named the night's refuge Camp Devastation, and no soul objected. The Masons gave us a Missouri country breakfast, in Missourian abundance, and we needed it: hot biscuits; hot 'wheat bread' prettily criss-crossed in a lattice pattern on top; hot corn-pone; fried chicken; bacon, coffee, eggs, milk, buttermilk, etc.; and the world may be confidently challenged to furnish the equal to such a breakfast, as it is cooked in the South.

We stayed several days at Mason's; and after all these years the memory of the dullness, the stillness and lifelessness of that slumberous farm-house still oppresses my spirit as with a sense of the presence of death and mourning. There was nothing to do, nothing to think about; there was no interest in life. The male part of the household were away in the fields all day, the women were busy and out of our sight; there was no sound but the plaintive wailing of a spinning-wheel, forever moaning out from some distant room, the most lonesome sound in nature, a sound steeped and sodden with homesickness and the emptiness of life. The family went to bed about dark every night, and as we were not invited to intrude any new customs, we naturally followed theirs. Those nights were a hundred years long to youths accustomed to being up till twelve. We lay awake and miserable till that hour every time, and grew old and decrepit waiting through the still eternities for the clock-strikes. This was no place for town boys. So at last it was with something very like joy that we received news that the enemy were on our track again. With a new birth of the old warrior spirit, we sprang to our places in line of battle and fell back on Camp Ralls.

Captain Lyman had taken a hint from Mason's talk, and he now gave orders that our camp should be guarded against surprise by the posting of pickets. I was ordered to place a picket at the forks of the road in Hyde's prairie. Night shut down black and threatening. I told Sergeant Bowers to go out to that place and stay till midnight; and, just as I was expecting, he said he wouldn't do it. I tried to get others to go, but all refused. Some

259

excused themselves on account of the weather; but the rest were frank enough to say they wouldn't go in any kind of weather. This kind of thing sounds odd now, and impossible, but there was no surprise in it at the time. On the contrary, it seemed a perfectly natural thing to do. There were scores of little camps scattered over Missouri where the same thing was happening. These camps were composed of young men who had been born and reared to a sturdy independence, and who did not know what it meant to be ordered around by Tom, Dick, and Harry, whom they had known familiarly all their lives, in the village or on the farm. It is quite within the probabilities that this same thing was happening all over the South. James Redpath recognized the justice of this assumption, and furnished the following instance in support of it. During a short stay in East Tennessee he was in a citizen colonel's tent one day, talking, when a big private appeared at the door, and without salute or other circumlocution said to the colonel,

'Say, Jim, I'm a-goin' home for a few days.'

'What for?'

'Well, I hain't b'en there for a right smart while, and I'd like to see how things is comin' on.'

'How long are you going to be gone?'

' 'Bout two weeks.'

'Well, don't be gone longer than that; and get back sooner if you can.'

That was all, and the citizen officer resumed his conversation where the private had broken it off. This was in the first months of the war, of course. The camps in our part of Missouri were under Brigadier-General Thomas H. Harris. He was a townsman of ours, a first-rate fellow, and well liked; but we had all familiarly known him as the sole and modest-salaried operator in our telegraph office, where he had to send about one dispatch a week in ordinary times, and two when there was a rush of business; consequently, when he appeared in our midst one day, on the wing, and delivered a military command of some sort, in a large military fashion, nobody was surprised at the response which he got from the assembled soldiery,

'Oh, now, what'll you take to *don't*, Tom Harris!'

It was quite the natural thing. One might justly imagine that we were hopeless material for war. And so we seemed, in our ignorant state; but there were those among us who afterward learned the grim trade; learned to obey like machines; became valuable soldiers; fought all through the war, and came out at the end with excellent records. One of the very boys who refused to go out on picket duty that night, and called me an ass for thinking he would expose himself to danger in such a foolhardy way, had become distinguished for intrepidity before he was a year older.

I did secure my picket that night – not by authority, but by diplomacy. I got Bowers to go, by agreeing to exchange ranks with him for the time being, and go along and stand the watch with him as his subordinate. We stayed out there a couple of dreary hours in the pitchy darkness and the rain, with nothing to modify the dreariness but Bowers's monotonous growlings at the war and the weather; then we began to nod, and presently found it next to impossible to stay in the saddle; so we gave up the tedious job, and went back to the camp without waiting for the relief guard. We rode into camp without interruption or objection from anybody, and the enemy could have done the same, for there were no sentries. Everybody was asleep; at midnight there was nobody to send out another picket, so none was sent. We never tried to establish a watch at night again, as far as I remember, but we generally kept a picket out in the daytime.

In that camp the whole command slept on the corn in the big corn-crib; and there was usually a general row before morning, for the place was full of rats, and they would scramble over the boys' bodies and faces, annoying and irritating everybody; and now and then they would bite someone's toe, and the person who owned the toe would start up and magnify his English and begin to throw corn in the dark. The ears were half as heavy as bricks, and when they struck they hurt. The persons struck would respond, and inside of five minutes every man would be locked in a death-grip with his neighbor. There was a grievous deal of blood shed in the corn-crib, but this was all that was spilt while I was in the war. No, that is not quite true. But for one circumstance it would have been all. I will come to that now.

Our scares were frequent. Every few days rumors would come that the enemy were approaching. In these cases we always fell back on some other camp of ours; we never stayed where we were. But the rumors always turned out to be false; so at last even we began to grow indifferent to them. One night a negro was sent to our corn-crib with the same old warning: the enemy was hovering in our neighborhood. We all said let him hover. We resolved to stay still and be comfortable. It was a fine war-like resolution, and no doubt we all felt the stir of it in our veins – for a moment. We had been having a very jolly time, that was full of horse-play and school-boy hilarity; but that cooled down now, and presently the fast-waning fire of forced jokes and forced laughs died out altogether, and the company became silent. Silent and nervous. And soon uneasy – worried – appre-hensive. We had said we would stay, and we were committed. We could have been persuaded to go, but there was nobody brave enough to suggest it. An almost noiseless movement presently began in the dark, by a general but unvoiced impulse. When the movement was completed, each man knew that he was not the only person who had crept to the front wall and had his eye at a crack between the logs. No, we were all there; all there with our hearts in our throats, and staring out toward the sugar-troughs where the forest foot-path came through. It was late, and was a deep woodsy stillness everywhere. There was a veiled moonlight, which was only just strong enough to enable us to mark the general shape of objects. Presently a muffled sound caught our ears, and we recognized it as the hoof-beats of a horse or horses. And right away a figure appeared in the forest path; it could have been made of smoke, its mass had so little sharpness of outline. It was a man on horseback; and it seemed to me that there were others behind him. I got hold of a gun in the dark, and pushed it through a crack between the logs, hardly knowing what I was doing, I was so dazed with fright. Somebody said 'Fire!' I pulled the trigger. I seemed to see a hundred flashes and hear a hundred reports, then I saw the man fall down out of the saddle. My first feeling was of surprised gratification; my first impulse was an apprentice-sportsman's impulse to run and pick up his game. Somebody said, hardly audibly, 'Good – we've got him! wait for the rest.' But the rest did not come. We waited – listened – still no more came. There was not a sound, not the whisper of a leaf; just perfect stillness; an uncanny kind

262

of stillness, which was all the more uncanny on account of the damp, earthy, late-night smells now rising and pervading it. Then, wondering, we crept stealthily out, and approached the man. When we got to him the moon revealed him distinctly. He was lying on his back, with his arms abroad; his mouth was open and his chest heaving with long gasps, and his white shirt-front was all splashed with blood. The thought shot through me that I was a murderer; that I had killed a man – a man who had never done me any harm. That was the coldest sensation that ever went through my marrow. I was down by him in a moment, helplessly stroking his forehead; and I would have given anything then – my own life freely – to make him again what he had been five minutes before. And all the boys seemed to be feeling in the same way; they hung over him, full of pitying interest, and tried all they could to help him, and said all sorts of regretful things. They had forgotten all about the enemy; they thought only of this one forlorn unit of the foe. Once my imagination persuaded me that the dying man gave me a reproachful look out of his shadowy eyes, and it seemed to me that I would rather he had stabbed me than done that. He muttered and mumbled like a dreamer in his sleep, about his wife and his child; and I thought with a new despair, 'This thing that I have done does not end with him; it falls upon *them* too, and they never did me any harm, any more than he.'

In a little while the man was dead. He was killed in war; killed in fair and legitimate war; killed in battle, as you may say; and yet he was as sincerely mourned by the opposing force as if he had been their brother. The boys stood there a half-hour sorrowing over him, and recalling the details of the tragedy, and wondering who he might be, and if he were a spy, and saying that if it were to do over again they would not hurt him unless he attacked them first. It soon came out that mine was not the only shot fired; there were five others, a division of the guilt which was a grateful relief to me, since it in some degree lightened and diminished the burden I was carrying. There were six shots fired at once; but I was not in my right mind at the time, and my heated imagination had magnified my one shot into a volley.

The man was not in uniform, and was not armed. He was a

stranger in the country; that was all we ever found out about him. The thought of him got to preying upon me every night; I could not get rid of it. I could not drive it away, the taking of that unoffending life seemed such a wanton thing. And it seemed an epitome of war; that all war must be just that – the killing of strangers against whom you feel no personal animosity; strangers whom, in other circumstances, you would help if you found them in trouble, and who would help you if you needed it. My campaign was spoiled. It seemed to me that I was not rightly equipped for this awful business; that war was intended for men, and I for a child's nurse. I resolved to retire from this avocation of sham soldiership while I could save some remnant of my self-respect. These morbid thoughts clung to me against reason; for at bottom I did not believe I had touched that man. The law of probabilities decreed me guiltless of his blood; for in all my small experience with guns I had never hit anything I had tried to hit, and I knew I had done my best to hit him. Yet there was no solace in the thought. Against a diseased imagination, demonstration goes for nothing.

The rest of my war experience was of a piece with what I have already told of it. We kept monotonously falling back upon one camp or another, and eating up the country. I marvel now at the patience of the farmers and their families. They ought to have shot us; on the contrary, they were as hospitably kind and courteous to us as if we had deserved it. In one of these camps we found Ab Grimes, an Upper Mississippi pilot, who afterwards became famous as a dare-devil rebel spy, whose career bristled with desperate adventures. The look and style of his comrades suggested that they had not come into the war to play, and their deeds made good the conjecture later. They were fine horsemen and good revolver-shots; but their favorite arm was the lasso. Each had one at his pommel, and could snatch a man out of the saddle with it every time, on a full gallop, at any reasonable distance.

In another camp the chief was a fierce and profane old blacksmith of sixty, and he had furnished his twenty recruits with gigantic home-made bowie-knives, to be swung with the two hands, like the *machetes* of the Isthmus. It was a grisly spectacle to see that earnest band practicing their murderous cuts and slashes under the eye of that remorseless old fanatic.

The last camp which we fell back upon was in a hollow near the village of Florida, where I was born – in Monroe County. Here we were warned, one day, that a Union colonel was sweeping down on us with a whole regiment at his heels. This looked decidedly serious. Our boys went apart and consulted; then we went back and told the other companies present that the war was a disappointment to us and we were going to disband. They were getting ready, themselves, to fall back on some place or other, and were only waiting for General Tom Harris, who was expected to arrive at any moment; so they tried to persuade us to wait a little while, but the majority of us said no, we were accustomed to falling back, and didn't need any of Tom Harris's help; we could get along perfectly well without him – and save time too. So about half of our fifteen, including myself, mounted and left on the instant; the others yielded to persuasion and stayed – stayed through the war.

An hour later we met General Harris on the road, with two or three people in his company – his staff, probably, but we could not tell; none of them were in uniform; uniforms had not come into vogue among us yet. Harris ordered us back; but we told him there was a Union colonel coming with a whole regiment in his wake, and it looked as if there was going to be a disturbance; so we had concluded to go home. He raged a little, but it was of no use; our minds were made up. We had done our share; had killed one man, exterminated one army, such as it was; let him go and kill the rest, and that would end the war. I did not see that brisk young general again until last year; then he was wearing white hair and whiskers.

In time I came to know that Union colonel whose coming frightened me out of the war and crippled the Southern cause to that extent – General Grant. I came within a few hours of seeing him when he was as unknown as I was myself; at a time when anybody could have said, 'Grant? Ulysses S. Grant? I do not remember hearing the name before.' It seems difficult to realize that there was once a time when such a remark could be rationally made; but there *was*, and I was within a few miles of the place and the occasion too, though proceeding in the other direction.

The thoughtful will not throw this war-paper of mine lightly aside as being valueless. It has this value: it is a not unfair picture of what went on in many and many a militia camp in the first months of the rebellion, when the green recruits were without discipline, without the steadying and heartening influence of trained leaders; when all their circumstances were new and strange, and charged with exaggerated terrors, and before the invaluable experience of actual collision in the field had turned them from rabbits into soldiers. If this side of the picture of that early day has not before been put into history, then history has been to that degree incomplete, for it had and has its rightful place there. There was more Bull Run material scattered through the early camps of this country than exhibited itself at Bull Run. And yet it learned its trade presently, and helped to fight the great battles later. I could have become a soldier myself, if I had waited. I had got part of it learned; I knew more about retreating than the man that invented retreating.